The Art of the Felt Maker

by

M. E. Burkett

Sponsored by

Crafts Advisory Committee   Northern Arts   Sotheby's

Abbot Hall Art Gallery
Kendal   Cumbria

THE ART OF THE FELT MAKER

The exhibition will be shown at the following venues:

Abbot Hall Art Gallery, Kendal	31 May-22 July 1979.
D.L.I. Museum and Arts Centre, Durham	28 July-2 September 1979.
Preston Hall Museum, Stockton-on-Tees	1-31 October 1979.
Royal Scottish Museum, Edinburgh	10 November-31 December 1979.
Leicester Museum and Art Gallery	1 February-31 March 1980.
Museum and Art Gallery, Warrington	14 April-30 May 1980.
Ashmolean Museum, Oxford	12 June-31 July 1980.
City Museum and Art Gallery, Bristol	27 September-1 November 1980.
Horniman Museum and Library, London	14 November 1980-14 February 1981.
War Memorial and Art Gallery, Stockport	March-April 1981.

ISBN 0 9503335 1 4

Printed by Titus Wilson & Son Ltd., Kendal

Contents

Catalogue

Foreword

Although felt is one of the earliest materials to have been made by man it has, until recently, received comparatively little scholarly attention. Perhaps its primitive nature, humble use amongst nomadic herdsmen, and lowly position on the floor, caused it to be neglected and despised among the rich cultures of successive generations. It is obvious from the attached bibliography that some travellers had been fascinated by it in the 18th and 19th centuries, but only recently has it received the attention, scientific and artistic, that it deserves. As in many fields, the interest in a subject can spring up simultaneously in many different parts of the world; so it is not surprising that at present there are people writing about felt in Canada, Denmark, France, Sweden and Russia. I have been fascinated by all aspects of felt-making since 1962 but only recently have discovered others with the same interest in the countries mentioned above. This exhibition is the result of continuing research and is probably the first ever to be devoted entirely to felt. I have included an extended bibliography and a selection of illustrations which widen the scope of the exhibition and could thus provide an introduction to those who would like to pursue the subject further.

Acknowledgements

Very sincere thanks are due to a large number of people without whose help this exhibition would not have been possible. First of all, Abbot Hall Art Gallery gratefully acknowledges the financial assistance of the Crafts Advisory Committee and Northern Arts (Crafts Panel) who have enabled us to purchase for the exhibition and print this catalogue; Sotheby's have generously supported the exhibition, and helped with publicity and promotion.

To the lenders we owe a great debt, especially considering the length of time for which they are sparing their possessions. We should like to record our thanks to The Whitworth Art Gallery, University of Manchester; Gulbenkian Museum of Oriental Art, University of Durham; Museum of Lakeland Life and Industry, Kendal; J. L. Wallworth and staff of Associated British Hat Manufacturers Ltd.; The British Museum; Vernon Park Museum, Stockport; Lord and Lady Oxmantown; Hordamuseet, Stend, Bergen; Professor Seton Lloyd; Katarina Ågren; Joss Graham; Peter Chorley; Peter Bennion of *Freewheelin',* Sheffield; I. R. Harvey of *Nomad Traders,* Cambridge; and those who wish to remain anonymous.

I am delighted to include a chapter on felt clothing by Dr. Veronika Gervers, Associate Curator of Textiles, Royal Ontario Museum, Toronto. Lennart Edelberg kindly allowed me to use material on felt-making in Afghanistan, and photographs taken while on the 3rd Danish Expedition to Central Asia, 1953. James Mellaart allowed the use of his unpublished information. Dr. May Beattie has given considerable advice on the catalogue; Helena Fialová, Milada Corvin, Dr. T. Barr, Mrs. Tamara Talbot Rice, and Mrs. Joan Allgrove are also to be thanked. Dr. Shirley Jarman, formerly Assistant Professor of the Asia Institute, Pahlavi University, Shiraz, contributed valuable information on felt rugs in Eastern Iran, and has allowed the use of her photographs.

For help in the collection of exhibits thanks go to Henrietta Moore and Jinny Allon, Dr. Abdul and Mrs. Gwen Khadjeh, C. W. Alp, J. D. Norton, Dr. R. Lawless, Sarah Bryant, Cem Ural, Andrew Wilson Young, Mrs. M. Wolpert, David Stronach and staff, Ralph Pinder-Wilson, Mrs. D. R. Stokes, Anthony Chew, Ali Afsari, Mrs. E. Chew, Alan Sekers, Mr. and Mrs. Isaac E. Asia, Teresa Shahbazi and Mrs. Golubeva, and the Novosti Press Agency for the loan of photographs.

Sincere thanks are due to C. L. Randall for making the model Türkmen tent; for further model making to Miss Finch-Dawson and Mrs. Lowther-Bouch, Sally Sekers, Mr. and Mrs. Walter and family; to Miss J. Glover, NWM & AGS, for examining the early felt specimens and for restoration; also for restoration: Miss M. Kelly, Mrs. D. Morris, and Mrs. Pat Short, who has in addition lent her own felts to the Exhibition.

For help in various directions over the manuscript: Lady Sekers, Miss R. Wade, Mrs. E. Chew, Mrs. J. Raikes, Professor R. J. Cramp, F. Darrehshouri, M. Bernard Dupaigne, Dr. M. Rogers, Dr. Hildegard Herzog, Mrs. W. Wightman; for typing the manuscript Miss J. Harvey, Mrs. O. McPherson; and finally for a great amount of research and general assistance with the completion of the final draft, thanks go to Miss V. A. J. Slowe, Robert W. H. Walker, John R. Renton and David W. Morris; and to Mr. R. Fielding and the staff of Titus Wilson for their expertise and patient co-operation.

Acknowledgements for plates and figures

Ibrahim Abdelmalek Pl. 57, Jinny Allon Pl. 10, Basel, Museum für Völkerkunde Pl. 32, Dr. May Beattie Pl. 56, Elizabeth Beazley Pls. 49, 55b, Bergen, Universitets-biblioteket Pl. 58 (reproduction rights K. Knudsen), Mary E. Burkett Pls. 1, 2, 9, 16, 24, 45-8, 50, 51; Col. Pls. 4b, 5b, 7, 8a, b; Ills. of Cat. Nos. 37, 46a, b, 53, Common Film, Helmut Wietz, Berlin Pls. 4, 5, 44 (all photographed by E. Höltzer), Copenhagen, Danish National Museum Pls. 26, 34, 35 (photographed by A. Bollerup Sørensen), Department of the Environment, London Pl. 59 (photographed by T. Middlemass) Crown Copyright – reproduced with permission of the Controller of Her Majesty's Stationery Office, Durham, Gulbenkian Museum of Oriental Art Ill. of Cat. No. 78, Lennart Edelberg Pls. 3a, b, 52a, b, 53a, b, 54, 55a, Lüfti Erkan Pl. 36, Michael Gervers Pls. 28-31, 37-43; Col. Pl. 5a, Dr. Veronika Gervers Supplementary diagram to Pl. 33, Dr. Shirley Jarman Ji-iii, back cover (© Dr. S. Jarman), Eileen Jay Fig. 23 (after Cowper, 1928), Louis D. Levine Col. Pl. 4a, James Mellaart Pls. 6, 7, 8, David W. Morris Figs. 2, 3, 5, 8-12, 16 (after Gervers, 1974), 18, 19, Novosti Press Agency, London Pls. 11, 13, 15, 19; Col. Pl. 1, Paris, Musée de l'homme Pl. 27 (photographed by M. Delaplanche), C. Leslie Randall Figs. 1, 4, 6, 7 (after drawing 52 in Wild, 1970, © Cambridge University Press), 13-15, 20-22; Ills. of Cat. Nos. 9a, b, 13a, b, 17a, b, 23-5, 29, 36, 41, 58-61, 87-9, 91, 105, 106a, 110, Tamara Talbot Rice Pls. 12, 14, 18 (from her *The Scythians,* Thames and Hudson, 1957), Derek Smith Ills. of Cat. Nos. 2-8, 11-12, 18, 19, 26a, 27, 40, 42, 43, 45, 47, 48, 49a, b, 50-2, 55a, b, 65, 69, 70, 73, 74, 76, 77, 79, 82, 85, 90, Stockport, Vernon Park Museum Pls. 60-65; Ill. of Cat. No. 96, Toronto, Royal Ontario Museum Pl. 33, Peter Wallum Ill. of Cat. No. 26b.

Chapter 1

TECHNICAL ANALYSIS OF FELTING

Over the centuries felt has been made in many countries for a great variety of uses. Pliny (VIII.73) said that compressed, well soaked in vinegar, it was capable of resisting iron and even fire. Papadopoulo-Vretos in 1845 made this statement to the Academy of Inscriptions and Letters in Paris: "I have macerated unbleached flax in vinegar saturated with salt, and after compression have obtained a felt with a power of resistance quite comparable with that of the famous armour of Conrad of Montferrat: seeing that neither the point of a sword nor even balls discharged from firearms were able to penetrate it" (Laufer, 1930, p. 18). Minor modifications in the actual making of it have crept in from one country to another, even from one tribe to another, but basically there is one unifying factor in its production. This is the simple scientific reason for wool becoming felt at all. Although it is not now such a common product in the West, apart from its use as underfelt or roofing felt and other industrial demands, it was, up to the 19th century, very widely used, especially in the hatting industry.

Descriptions of its manufacture were therefore common in encyclopaedias such as Tomlinson's *Encyclopaedia of Useful Arts and Manufactures* (1854), where it was described thus:

> Wool is one of the few fibers which has the unique property of being able to felt. This is a desirable feature in milling and scouring and for felt-making, but undesirable in all-wool styles, such as stockings, sweaters, swim-suits and other garments. This has been partly overcome by the chlorination process which uses dilute solutions of chlorine and can be employed at most stages of manufacturing. *It is not fully understood why felting occurs but it may be a result of the tension existing in the wool, the peculiar serrated shape of the outer layers of the fiber made by the pointed-tip overlapping scales, and the chemical characteristics of the cystine linkages.* Wool is sensible to alkali damage, but more resistant to acid than cotton or the vegetable fibers. Felting may be regarded as a non-woven material and, therefore, pressed felt is one of the oldest forms of non-woven fabric. This type of fabric is built up of the interlocking of fiber and requires no bonding agent. The fibers become stably intermeshed by a combination of mechanical work, chemical action, moisture and heat.

A greater scientific knowledge of its chemical process has been acquired in this century. *Briefly, the ability of wool fibres in the mass to felt, is attributed to their unique property of "creeping" in a tip to root direction under pressure.* This phenomenon was first described by a French scientist, Monge, who believed that it was due to the scaly outer covering of the fibres (Fig. 1). These scales grow round the fibre like over-lapping roof tiles with their free edges inclined towards the fibre tip. When a single fibre is rubbed between the finger and thumb in the direction of its length, it can be seen to travel backwards from its tip, and in a manner rather aptly described as similar to a worm crawling. While the direction of this "creep" is due to the orientation and relative rigidity of the scales, the worm-like movement is the outcome of the in-built elasticity of the fibre.

Fig. 1: Close-up of a wool fibre showing scales. Magnification by 750.

This elasticity is a structure sequence of ingenious mechanisms. First there is the natural crimp or curl of the wool fibre, which varies according to the breed, age and nutritional state of the sheep, but is always present to some degree. It is caused by the segregation of the outer (cortical) cells of the fibre into two adjoining hemicylindrical longitudinal bundles. Because the principle constituent of these cells, the protein keratin, is well matured and hardened in one of these bundles, and immature and soft in the other, the rigidity of the former lying in close contact with the pliability of the other, results in not only the curl of the fibre but, with the hemicylinders twisting upon their own axes within the fibre, the fibre profile is correspondingly twisted.

Secondly, electron microscopic studies have shown that the long chain keratin molecules, spiral not only within their own axes but, molecule against molecule, are coiled like a spring and capable of recoil. The integrity of this molecular stretch mechanism is dependent upon the cross links of the keratin chains. These can be damaged by excess of heat, strong alkalis, bleaching agents and sulphuric acid. The cross-links help to maintain the folded structure of these chains and at the same time to keep them intact as they stretch. Both the "creep" and the elasticity of the fibre mass are increased by warmth and the moisture of weakly alkaline solutions during the application of intermittent firm pressure. These movements cause the fibre mass to become ever more tightly entangled and to form a homogeneous layer of felt (Cook, 1968, Vol. 1, Ill. on pp. 98, 104, 112).

Although the scientific implications behind felt-making were probably never realised by the Asian nomadic peoples who made the most use of it, they fully exploited its possibilities. Depending on the quality of the wool used, it was made both extremely thick or very fine. In fact, felt of up to a thickness of one inch was described by Edmond O'Donovan (O'Donovan, 1882, Vol. 1, p. 42) for nomads' tent coverings (see also p. 42). The finest I have seen are fragments from the village of Pazyryk in Siberia, now in the Hermitage Museum in Leningrad. Even allowing for the inevitable shrinkage over the years, they vary from 1/16″ to 1/10″.

Pl. 1: Feltmaker's bow, Shiraz, 1966.

In most parts of Asia sheep's wool is used for felting. It can be mixed with goat hair and is often quite coarse. Camel hair and other finer hair is often used for making felt caps. In Iran, and also in Turkey and Afghanistan, the sheep are usually clipped twice a year, in the late spring and late summer. At high altitudes the shearing may take place only once a year; the wools are of three main colours, natural or ivory, light brown, and dark brown. The longer wools and ivory are more highly valued than the browns. Sometimes sheep-washing is done before shearing, but otherwise the wool is seldom washed before carding. It is however, sorted by hand, often by children, into bundles of different colours and the dirt removed as far as possible. It is then judged how much is required for a particular object, and weighed. A bow (Pl. 1) and a wooden mallet are then used to separate the wool and loosen the tangles. The string of the bow, made of gut, is laid horizontally just above the layer of wool, and beaten with the mallet, a process which, by creating strong vibrations, produces the effect of carding, making the wool fluffy and porous. In more recent times, carding machines have been introduced to do this more quickly, but the early felt-makers used the bow. These heavy objects may not easily be found now save in hat-making shops in Isfahan, Shiraz and other towns, (see p. 44 and fig. 2).

Fig. 2: Feltmaker's bow in use.

The preparation of an unpatterned felt is straightforward. In Türkmen examples two women alternately beat the wool with long sticks (*çirpa*). The Türkmen then card the wool on a large comb with two rows of fine metal teeth facing upwards, placed on a firm base. A wad of wool is forced downwards on to the teeth, then pulled apart (Abbot Hall Art Gallery, 1971, p. 31). This is repeated until the wool is in suitable condition for felt-making. It takes some time to do this, especially to make the felts – usually white – for covering the tent; for each tent cover it takes six women several days. Enough wool is then beaten out loosely on the ground, sometimes in very hot weather, under a makeshift tent. Reed mats (*qamís*), similar to those encircling the tents themselves, are laid on the ground first, or sometimes a bed of leaves, or even an old *kilim,* sacking, or old felts, are spread out. (Hat makers do not use reed mats but work the felt on a metal former). According to what is being made, enough wool is weighed and placed on the matting. In some areas solid or liquid soap is sprinkled or spread over the matting first. The shape of the article or garment is also taken into consideration and the wool either laid in a rectangle for a mat, or trapezoidal shape for some of the tent pieces. In Turkey, when making a felt coat, *kepenek,* (Ch. 6) a long strip is made with extra width and length for the back and less for the front, which would later be cut for the vent. The wool, depending on the required final thickness, is piled either low or high accordingly, and can be up to 40 cms. thick at this stage.

In Turkey, the 'master' of the operation – but in Afghanistan, Russia and Persia often the woman in charge – ensures that the wool is correctly arranged and the mass of the correct size, and then sprinkles it with hot water. The whole felt is then rolled up tightly and tied, in order to compress the wool, care being taken to do it evenly; sometimes more than one felt was included in the same roll, so giving even more pressure. In Afghanistan, the men then roll the bundle with their feet; in Turkey, Iran and Iraq, the women usually roll with their forearms, kneeling in a row and pushing the roll back and forth (Pl. 2). Sometimes additional force is exerted by knees or feet. For up to an hour this pressure is applied evenly from end to end of the roll. The very large early carpets, made more often in previous centuries, required up to twenty or more men and women. After this, the roll is untied, unevennesses of thickness padded out, the edges straightened, and sometimes turned over to make them regular. More hot water, soap or soapwort are applied and the rolling begins again, at right angles to the first direction, and continues for three or four hours. This process cannot be left till the next day or the wool will not be "cooked" or felted (see p. 87). In order to keep the rhythm constant, one of the workers used to lead a monotonous chant, *Hih Hih Hih* in Turkey, and various forms of songs, now lost, in other countries. After the final rolling had been done, a short prayer

Pl. 2: Türkmen women rolling felt near Gunbad-i-Qabus, 1970.

used sometimes to be said before the final unwrapping of the bundle. When patterned rugs are made, the wool for the pattern has to be laid on the matting first and the rest of the wool laid on top of it. In some places the pattern is delineated by laying strands of wool to guide the maker as to where to put the colour (Pl. 3a, b). Then small rolls of dyed wool are placed in the spaces defined, and more wool placed in the gaps. When enough wool has been piled on top of the rug, another pattern is sometimes superimposed which will eventually appear underneath the rug. This varies from lattice patterns to an arrangement of dots. Then the felt, either plain or decorated, has to be fulled as it is still very rough after the first rolling. In Turkey this used to be done in the baths (*hammams*), where, in the hot steamy atmosphere, the felts were rolled back and forth on the marble floors. Soap and water are again used and the workers do not stop until the fibres are properly matted together. Sometimes resin is added for extra solidification.

Finally, the finished article has to be rubbed smooth by hand, and the soap, (if used, which was not always the case) washed out. The rubbing used to be done by wooden and smooth stone rollers, or polished flat stones. Many of the various activities mentioned in this section can be seen in Plate 5, a photograph taken by Ernst Höltzer (1835-1911) in Isfahan.

The finished felt is solid, impervious to water and, if tent covers, white. The latter gradually darkened to black in a few years with the constant smoke. Carpets and rugs survive longer but only withstand the wear of bare feet. They can last up to fifty years; in some places worn felts would be re-used.*

* The Baskirs of the Urals used to make felt by a method which differed interestingly in several respects from that described above. To facilitate the rolling of the wetted wool to make it felt together, it was wrapped around a smooth pole; intensive rolling of the felt was done by placing it on a bench, where it was rolled back and forth by twelve to fifteen girls who stood for the task, thus applying more pressure; while still on the bench the felt was thoroughly beaten all over with the hands (Laszlo, 1944; reference supplied by Lady Sekers).

Pl. 3a: Setting out the pattern with clumps of white wool.

Pl. 3b: Laying strands from a ball as extra guide lines.

Pls. 4, 5: Two general views of felt-making in Isfahan at the end of the 19th century. (Plate 5 overleaf.)

Chapter 2

ARCHAEOLOGICAL EVIDENCE FOR THE EARLIEST FELTS

Pl. 6: Shrine wall at Çatal Hüyük.

Legendary origins have been handed down in each felt-making country, but there could have been many natural causes for its invention. It is unlikely we shall ever know.

> The origins of felt in Persia are ascribed to Solomon's son who was a shepherd. He was sure that his sheep's wool could be made into waterproof mats without the aid of a loom, but try as he might he could not make the fibres stick together. In the end he rather naturally lost his temper, and stamped about on the fleece crying large tears of frustration. And behold! He had discovered felt.

Although the origin of felt is unknown, in all probability it is the earliest form of textile, and, like most, has a low survival rate in archaeological conditions.* Specimens from the earlier millennia rarely come to light. It is from the Central Asian Steppes that archaeologists have so far found the oldest examples. Felt has been produced there before and since *c.* 600 B.C., by which time man had discovered how to make textiles from spinning and weaving. It was used for clothing and mats, and the preference for it for protection instead of woven textiles has long been known. (It is, of course, a non-woven fabric, and should not be referred to in the same terms as a woven textile).

The many scattered references to felt tell us little about its origins. The finds, especially those at Pazyryk, show a highly developed technology and a

* It is quite possible that Jacob made Joseph's coat of felt: (a) felting would have been the earliest method of making a multi-coloured coat; (b) Jacob himself made the coat – men often made felt; (c) 'many' (A. V. Genesis Ch. 37 v. 3) implies 'many pieces'.

great diversity in design and execution. However, none of these finds predates the Iron Age, and many of them date from the first millennium A.D.

The earliest indication of the knowledge of felt occurred when, in 1965, James Mellaart conducted a fourth season of excavations at Çatal Hüyük in Turkey (Mellaart, 1966, (1) & (2)). He was aiming to investigate the lowest levels of the ancient site of Çatal Hüyük, a settlement which is of pre-eminent importance for the Neolithic Age. Excavations revealed the nearest thing to a city ever found of that period, the levels showing an amazing continuity over the years from approximately 6500/6300 B.C. That the city was populous is apparent from the large number of buildings and the continuous reconstructions and rebuilding in each level. A thriving agricultural economy with a fine and very early system of irrigation was evident. Some of the discoveries of the 1965 season and subsequent studies of the zoological remains (Perkins, 1969) are relevant to the subject of this catalogue and the possible uses of felt at the site.

On the interior wall of a shrine, measuring 6×4·5 m, on the north of the site, (Mellaart, 1966, (2) p. 179, Fig. 7), was a remarkable wall painting, (Pl. 6).

"Bordered by a red honeycomb pattern at its western end, the painting is divided into five panels by parallel vertical lines. Within each panel there are whirling curvilinear motifs of a type as yet unknown at Çatal Hüyük (Pl. 7). On a white ground the patterns are drawn in a buff-brown colour, outlined in black. Both patterns and edging technique are strongly reminiscent of felt appliqué", (this idea was confirmed by Mr. Harold Burnham), "and the identification of actual felt among the textiles from graves in Level VI adds weight to the suggestion that this material was known to the neolithic people of Çatal Hüyük" (Mellaart, 1966, (2), p. 180).*

Each panel measured roughly 1 m. in width by 0·75 m. high, but the upper parts of the wall had gone, so the original height cannot be calculated. To the extreme right of the panel, a textile type pattern (Pl. 6) in black illustrates fishing nets (Mellaart, 1966, (2), Pl. XLIIIb). There were other wall paintings indicating a wealth of

* Hans Helbaek, paleoethnobotanist, while partaking in the excavations at Çatal Hüyük in 1963, identified felt remains in Level VI. There was no sign of pattern, but it proved to be animal hair, pressed together. In this context it may be worth noticing that at Beycesultan, Seton Lloyd and James Mellaart found thick patches of felt in the floors of early Bronze Age, now *c.* 3000-2700 B.C. (information from J. Mellaart, not yet published).

Pl. 7: Detail of wall painting at Çatal Hüyük.

material in relation to the study of textiles. Several paintings included motifs used on modern Anatolian rugs and *kilims*. In the conservation of textiles recovered it was discovered that some pieces of fabric were sewn neatly together, which is rare for the period.* When the wall surface illustrated in Plate 6 was removed, another wall painting was found beneath it. This featured a further remarkable design (Pl. 8), illustrated here in a felt reconstruction, published first in 1977.†

Pl. 8: Reconstruction in felt of wall painting found behind that in Plate 7.

* Textiles from Level VI A and B are all well dated through a series of radio-carbon dates which give an average of 5700±100 for Level VI A, and an average of 5867±100 for Level VI B: J. Mellaart: *Neolithic of the Near East*, London 1975, p. 285; c.f. H. Burnham, "Çatal Hüyük: the Textiles and Twine Fabrics". *Anatolian Studies*, XV (1965), pp. 169-74.

† This reconstruction in felt was made by Miss Raymonde Enderley, Senior Conservationist Officer, British Museum Department of Conservation, who was on the site. It is published here by permission of Mr. Mellaart and Miss Enderley, who have allowed me to have it photographed and provided me with information about felt at Çatal Hüyük and Beycesultan. Miss Enderley herself traced the clear but faint pattern from the wall. *Anatolian Studies*, vol. XXVII, 1977, Miss M. E. Burkett.

Literary allusions to felt are, as I shall mention later, of a much later date. Obviously archaeological interpretations of paintings depend for final proof on contemporary material evidence. Nevertheless, ethnographic parallels from other periods can support a high degree of probability. An analysis of the designs of both wall paintings serves to confirm their likeness to felt which Mellaart commented on, but did not substantiate.

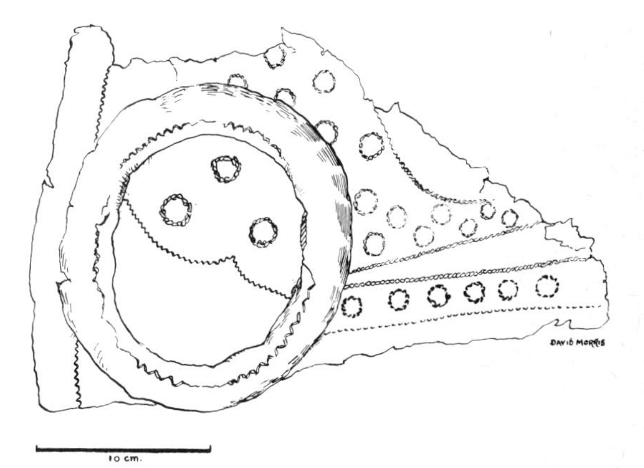

Fig. 3: Felt-covered ring stand.

Clearly these finds by James Mellaart are of great importance to the dating of the earliest examples of felt, and in time it is hoped that others will come to light.

In the National Museum of Copenhagen, there are caps, often referred to as of a sturdy felt, preserved from *c.* 1600 B.C. – the early Bronze Age – and coming from North Slesvig and Jutland. However, the Danish National Museum now informs me that these items are not made of felt but are tabby woven. Bronze Age scraps of felt have been found in Germany; Sir Aurel Stein found small pieces in his travels in Asia (Stein, 1907, 1921 and 1928).

The most exciting examples were found when the stone burial chambers in the Altai mountains in Siberia were opened early this century. Ice and the absence of air had preserved the contents of two hundred and twelve tumuli, including a prince's tomb where, as well as fragments, there were two fine felt rugs. These Pazyryk mounds yielded a magnificent array of items from the period 7th-2nd century B.C. Because of the icy conditions of permafrost, the material was in amazingly good order (Rudenko, 1970). The list recorded by Rudenko among the Pazyryk finds includes wall carpets; covers for the body and linings for sarcophagi; socks for men and women; stockings; cushions stuffed with deer hair; horse bits; little felt-covered metal rings for making spherical-bottomed vessels of wood, pottery, silver, gold or glass stand upright (Fig. 3); men's outer shirts; and women's hair accessories (lumps of felt over which they curled their hair). Felt was also used for decoration (or what would appear at first glance to be decoration) on saddles, bows, saddle covers, blankets, masks and mane covers for horses, and the interior and exterior of tents (Pl. 9, 10 and Ch. 5). The great Pazyryk felt is by far the earliest important surviving example of this ancient craft. It is also the largest (4·5 ×6·5 m) and is housed in the Pazyryk room of the Hermitage Museum, Leningrad (Pl. 11). As it is so remarkable it may be worth considering it in some detail. On a natural ground two rows of figures are separated by three bands of floral patterns, and the felt is applied in various colours. The figures represent a seated goddess with a masculine face, thought by Rudenko to be Tabiti or Apia (Rudenko, 1970, p. 290), holding a sacred branch in her hand, and a male rider approaching her on horseback (Col. Pl. 1 and Pl. 12). This pair is repeated six times with a suggestion of further repeats which have been cut. On the right hand side of the felt there appears to have been a border with representations of an elaborate bird and winged animal (Fig. 4). Both motifs have been cut and possibly some was lost during excavation and restoration. A sphinx, a winged and antlered half-human, half-lion in applied felt was also found in the same barrow (Meister, 1936, p. 4750).* K. Jettmar points out that the same goddess was also found in the Pontic area. Some Russians considered it to be Anahita of the Medes and Persians (Jettmar, 1967, p. 138).

* Bulls, griffons, mythological monsters are seen on other artifacts from central Asia. They are frequently inlaid in metals on brooches and other artifacts.

Pl. 9: Exterior of modern *yurt* near Gunbad-i-Qabus, 1970.

But the subject matter is only of importance here in relation to its provenance and origins. The method of construction is of great interest. It is obvious that all the techniques of felt-making were used – appliqué, mosaic, inlay and embroidery. Different materials such as wood and metal plaques were combined in the designs of pieces found in some of the other barrows. A wide range of colours was used and these barrows alone furnish examples of over 30 different types of items made in felt. A selection of these items appeared in "Frozen Tombs", an exhibition at the British Museum, November 1978-February 1979.

Despite the fact that the measurements of the great felt are given by Rudenko, it is not until one is face to face with it, on the wall in the Hermitage, that one realises its immense size. It is 4·5×6·5 m and occupies one wall in the display of these spectacular finds from the Altai region (Tomb no. 5).

As mentioned by Rudenko in his assessment of its function, it must have been meant to hang vertically, because the design is pictorial, the rows of figures appearing one above the other, unlike the knotted pile carpet from the same burial (Pl. 13). In the latter the field is non-directional in design but the processional border adjacent to the viewer, standing near the carpet, is always pictorially correct (Rudenko, 1970, p. 64). In referring to the great felt as a carpet it must be noted that as yet there is no evidence for what purpose it was to serve. It was found rolled up among the horse gear in the tomb. Scholars at the Hermitage have in an attempted reconstruction shown it as a hanging, but Dr. Richard Barnett said: "It would have been big enough to cover the entire burial of horses, cart and chariot, if that is how it was used here". (Barnett, 1953, pp. 69-70; 1955, p. 26). It was with reference to its probable use that I examined it in 1977. There seem to be five main possibilities: (a) as a tomb cover, (b) as an interior wall of a cart-dwelling on wheels such as those described by Herodotus (Herodotus IV, 46, 114, 121) (Pl. 14), (c) as the deceased's tomb hanging, (d) for the interior of a house (used as a hanging behind his seat or throne during the owner's lifetime), (e) for use in the afterworld.

Its use (a) as a cover for a tomb (or cart or tent) would have been unlikely as the rows of figures already mentioned would not have been seen properly. To take (c) next; the dimensions of the tomb in association with which it was recovered were too small to have allowed

Pl. 10: Interior of modern *yurt* near Gunbad-i-Qabus, 1978.

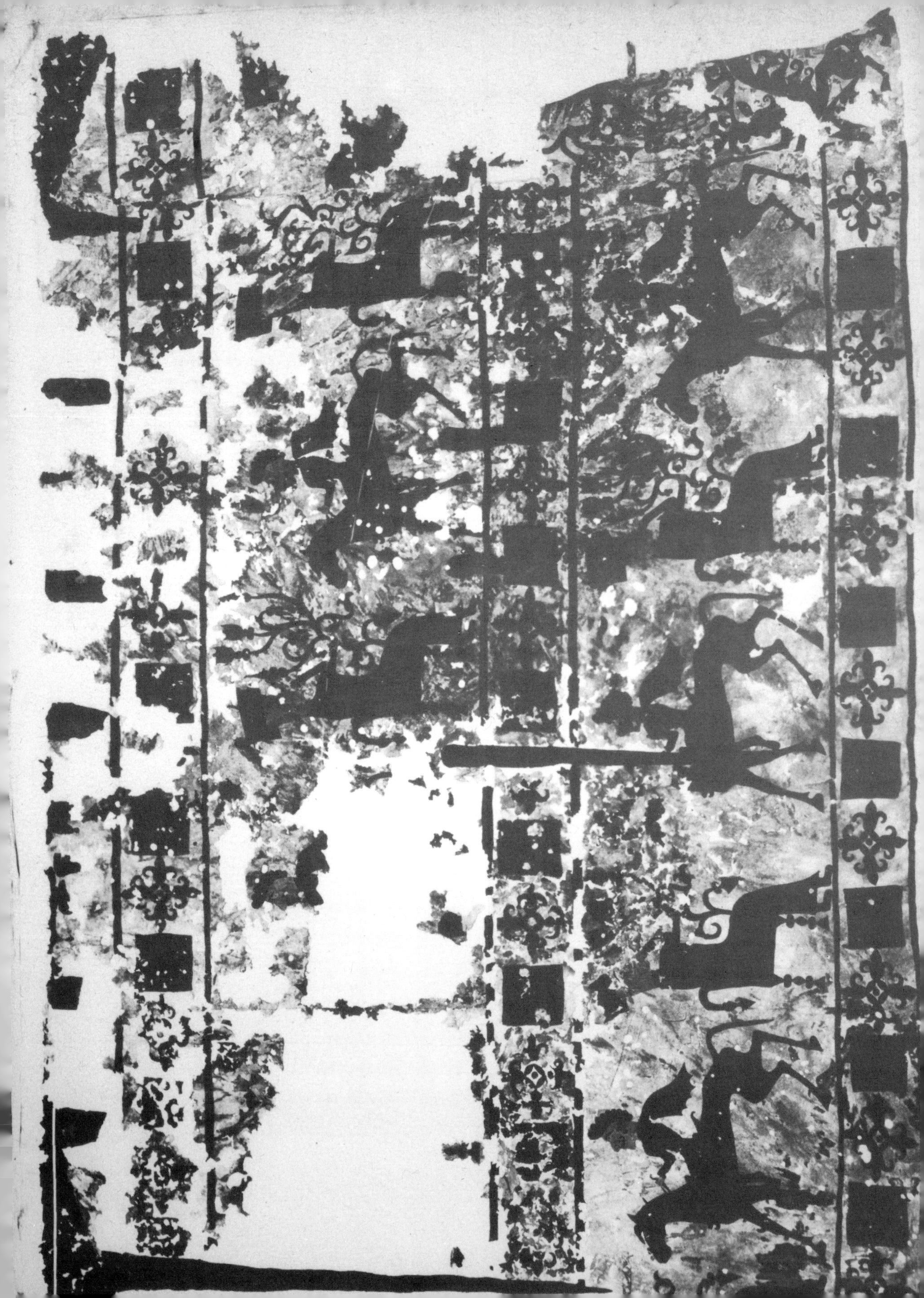

this to be a wall hanging. Barrow 5 measured 2·3×1·4 m high internally (Rudenko, 1970, p. 324). One fact bears mention, the roof of the coffin in barrow 5 was gabled unlike the roofs of the others which were domed. In (e) there are not such simple grounds on which to dismiss the suppositions. Who knows what was the intention in the after world, but whatever it was it might have been based on an imitation or enlarged version of the known world in which the buried man had lived.

We may at first discount (b) fairly rapidly, as the wagon would have had to be enormous to move a building, of which one wall was 4·5×6·5 m. In Herodotus' description, the carts were 4 or 6 wheeled, sometimes described as small and inhabited by the women (Herodotus IV, 46, 114, 121 and Rudenko, 1970, p. 324) and it would seem to have been impractical for the horses involved to have drawn such a large vehicle. However, in Pl. 14* the vast size of cart-houses later in Mongol times may mean they already had such large moving homes. It might have covered the interior wall of a circular tent either on or off a cart, the two vertical bands of mythological animals serving as protective symbols inside the doorway as at Persepolis where carved royal heroes fighting animals guard all entrances.

* Cf. Tamara Talbot Rice, *The Seljuks,* plate 33. Although the cart dwellings in this illustration are of 1253 A.D. they might have had similar structures.

Pl. 12: Detail of male rider approaching seated figure.

◄ Pl. 11: The Pazyryk Felt.

Fig. 4: Detail of part of the great felt (after restoration).

So it is to (d) I would like to turn. It could have been used as a hanging in the real world for a rectangular wall (and we have established that it probably was used as a hanging). It might even have been a divider between two rooms. The form of it, judging from the two triangular pieces of dark brown felt (see Chap. 4, p. 21) on the top two corners, suggests that it was following the form of a large gabled roof. (It has been noted that the tomb in Barrow 5 was gabled). In this case the two dark pieces of felt may have been gripped by rafters, so holding it up under the ceiling, but there is insufficient evidence to draw any firm conclusion. Perhaps this particular tomb could have been reflecting in miniature a large gabled house. It is likely that the felt may in fact have been made as an even larger piece despite the fact that it must have taken about 15 people to roll it (Pl. 4). It must certainly have been larger originally, as it would seem more natural to have put a whole woman on the seat on the lower left corner for example, and whole mythological animals. It is tempting to return to (b) and see it as the interior hanging in a large cart tent on wheels. One other interesting possibility remains. The dark brown vertical lines on it interpreted by Russian scholars as signs of mourning could be interpreted in two other ways (Pl. 11): they could be in some way related to the timber structure of the building in which it was to hang, or just conceivably be connected with the ancient forms of teats mentioned by Carpini (cf. Chap. 4, p. 21).

The next major felt find was at Noin Ula in Northern Mongolia. The burial site was situated 1500 metres above sea level. In tumulus No. 6 there were felt floor and ceiling carpets, in appliqué of felt and other materials. The larger of the two specimens has a central panel consisting of 24 spirals and a frieze of animals in combat (Fig. 5, Pl. 15). The presence of a dated lacquer bowl enabled them to be ascribed to the first decade of

Pl. 14: Cart dwelling on wheels after a drawing by Friar William of Rubruck.

Pl. 13: Part of woven carpet found in Mound 5, Pazyryk.

the 1st century A.D. (Jettmar, 1967). A comprehensive study on this has been written by W. Meister (Meister, 1931-6).*

The remarkable Shosoin treasures of the 8th century A.D. excavated about 1930 in Japan, are second only to the Noin Ula finds in the Altai. The objects found, including felt, provide important evidence for the spread of Sasanian ideas to Chinese, and thence to Japanese, art forms. They also include Sasanian artifacts which must have travelled East with the last of the Sasanian Kings. Yazdijird III's family fled to China after the Moslem invasion, and in fact was allowed to hold government appointments in China (Mostafavi, 1960).

* In 1967/8 John Hansman found felt at Qūmis near Damghan which by its association with a Sasanian coin can be dated to sometime before the 7th year of the reign of Hormizd IV, *c.* 586 A.D. (Cat. No. 1).

There were also some very interesting saddle cloths and horse furniture. In the East, the saddle cloth did not exist for the comfort of the rider but because the saddle, which was made of wood, would have hurt the horse (Fig. 6a, b). Felt was the ideal solution because of its great thickness, but sometimes two cloths were used to protect the animals, and a ventilation space was left between the saddle and the saddle cloth. This was a fundamental difference between eastern and western horse furniture, and even today, there is still a great deal of wood in the simple donkey saddles of Turkey (Sudzuki, 1960).

Osamu Sudzuki traces back the seat bars and saddles through the Sasanian period to those among the Pazyryk finds and shows how the latter had influenced the saddles and horse furniture found in the Shosoin treasure at Nara.

Fig. 5: Detail of the central panel showing spirals.

Pl. 15: Detail of two creatures in combat (after restoration). Note appliqué and mosaic techniques.

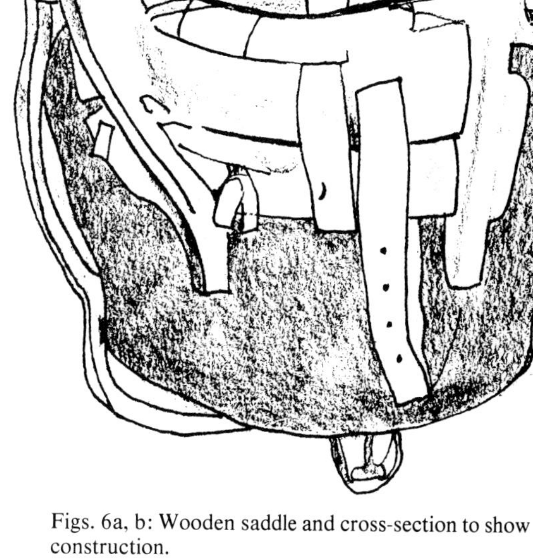

Figs. 6a, b: Wooden saddle and cross-section to show construction.

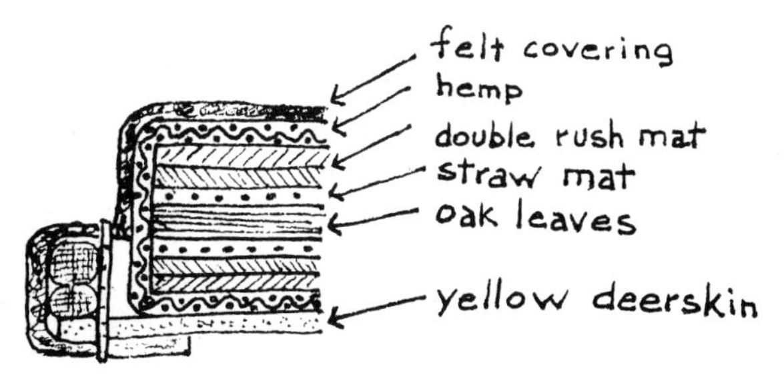

Fig. 6b.

Chapter 3

THE HISTORY OF FELT FROM WRITTEN SOURCES

Literary references to the use of felt in China go back to 2300 B.C., when warriors were known to protect themselves with felt shields, hats and other clothes, and to use felt boats. Frequent references to its use prove that it continued to be used in China well into this century, when Laufer found many felt-making industries still functioning (Laufer, 1930, pp. 3-7).

Mentions of felt in classical literature are numerous. The Greek word for felt, *pilos,* refers to felt cloth, or anything made of felt. In Homer's *Iliad* felt caps are described, and Odysseus was said to have worn a helmet lined with felt (Homer, *Il.* X, 265). Hesiod (Works and Days 540) mentions shoes made of felt (as does Plato in the Symposium 220B), also skull-caps like a fez (Works and Days 544); Herodotus refers several times to felt: he remarks the Persians' habit of wearing felt skull-caps (3.12 – he thought it explained the thinness of their skulls!); a particular Scythian tribe, he notes, used bands of thick white felt to protect their fruit trees (4.23). Thucydides (4.34) refers to cuirasses made of felt. Aristophanes compares a cock's comb with a Persian cap, *kurbasia* (The *Birds* 487). The King wore a taller and stiffer version of this cap. Xenophon describes the subjects, 'their tiaras folded and bent forward'. Strabo describes the tall felt caps worn by Achaemenian soldiers as the shape of a tower (Pl. 16). He recorded that Nearchus, who was with Alexander the Great on his journey east to India as Admiral of the Fleet in 325 B.C., found that the Indians already knew the art of felt-making from wool (Strabo, XV, 1, 67 & 3, 15). At the funeral of Alexander in 324 B.C. the pyre was draped with a piece of scarlet felt. Strabo also describes the Scythians as living in carts used as houses and draped with felt (cf. Chap. 2, p. 13).

Pl. 16: Achaemenian soldiers, Persepolis.

In fact, it is to felt's use in Central Asia that one finds the most abundant references. It must have been vital to every aspect of daily life (Laufer, 1930, pp. 7-16). Perhaps at all times in Greece, felt hats were particularly popular: later writers mention the Arcadian, Laconian and Macedonian styles of felt hat. Lacedaimonian cloaks were made of felt, called in Latin *coacta,* (Tomlinson, 1854).

From the Greeks, felt no doubt passed easily to the Romans, as there are frequent references in Latin literature to its production and use. Tight-fitting caps were worn by the soldiers when attending theatres and festivals or even eating. Slaves, when given their freedom, used to shave their heads and wear felt caps, so that the word "felt" became synonymous with freedom and the common saying "to call to the felt caps" meant to call the slaves to freedom (Laufer, 1930). A coin celebrating the assassination of Julius Caesar in 44 B.C. shows a felt cap flanked by two daggers (Olschki, 1949, pp. 45-6). When Nero died in 68 A.D., the streets of Rome were full of the common people wandering happily about the streets, referred to by Suetonius in his *Life of Nero* as "the felted mob" (*plebs pileata*). The figure of Liberty on the coins of Antoninus Pius (138-161 A.D.) holds the cap in her right hand.

The earliest surviving recorded illustration of felt-making is probably the splendid wall-painting outside Verecundus' workshop in Pompeii (Fig. 7) (Wild, 1970, drawing 52).

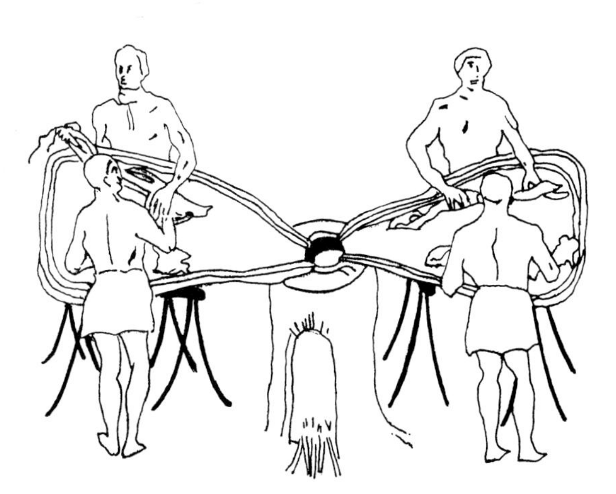

Fig. 7: Mural of felt-making outside Verecundus' workshop in Pompeii.

Through T'ang writers we first hear of felt in Tibet for plates and clothing, as well as tents (*fu-lu* in Chinese; *sbra* in Tibetan), including large ones for the army camps. Chinese clay tomb figurines of the Sui and T'ang Dynasties are often depicted wearing what appear to be felt caps (Gervers-Molnár, 1973, Figs. 25-29). T'ang Dynasty annals also record at the beginning of the T'ien-pao period (742-756 A.D.) that white felt was amongst the gifts sent from the Court of the King of Ceylon. It is also noted that on the island of Java, two kinds of felt were available, one dyed a colour like granite and the other deep crimson (Laufer, 1930, p. 8).

For the Sung period (960-1280 A.D.) official annals provide evidence of the importing of felt from the north western empire of the Tanguts, which included the Kukunoor area, Kansu and Ninghsia. There is an amusing anecdote, "a famous writer was asleep when burglars broke in and began searching for loot. When they were ready to go he said calmly, 'Gentlemen, the blue felt carpet there is a family heirloom, you might at least leave me that!' The robbers immediately fled in panic!"

Under Mongol rule, much documentation is available and many elaborate felts were made as this description of the carpets from Ninghsia shows: "In the year 1299, felt carpets with an area of 331 square metres were manufactured for the Palace of the Special Chambers" (Imperial harem). A generation later, we read that seven carpets measuring together 8050 square feet were delivered to the Palace in the same year, 1325; the Imperial ancestral hall was furnished with five felt carpets with "floral patterns in appliqué work". (Bidder, 1964, pp. 87-91).

Johannes de Plano Carpini gives a vivid description of felted tents when he visited the court of Küyük Khan from 1245-1247 A.D.

> Their walls be covered with felt. Their doors are made of felt also .... Their manners are partly prayse-worthie and partly detestable .... They purified their beds, carts and felts in fire if polluted ... In the land of the foresayd Karakytayans, Occoday Cham, the sonne of Chingis Cham, after he was created Emperor, built a certaine citie, on the south side, there is an huge desert, wherein wilde men are certainely reported to inhabite, which cannot speake at all, and are destitute of joyntes in their legges, so that if they fall, they cannot rise alone by themselves. Howbeit, they are of discretion to make felts of Camels haire wherewith they clothe themselves, and which they hold against the winde. And if any time the Tartars pursuing them, chance to wound them with their arrowes, they put herbes into their wounds and fly strongly before them. (Carpini, 1900).

There may be legend in this story but at least it serves to show that the felts were probably used exactly in the same way as they are today, as complete protection from all ills, wind, rain and battle.

Genghis Khan's collective designation for the unified Turko-Mongolian tribes of Asia was "the generations that live in felt tents" (Olschki, 1949, p. 14). Marco Polo described rain-proof black felt, and in the 14th century Ibn Batuta actually travelled in a four-wheeled wagon upon which "was placed a sort of pavilion of wands, laced together with narrow thongs; it was covered with felt". He enjoyed his journey in it as there were windows and he could admire the scenery or read, write or sleep as they travelled along (Krist, 1938, and Hakluyt, 1903, p. 243) (cf. p. 18 of this chapter for Strabo's comment on the Scythians and Chap. 2, p. 13).

Captain John Smith, in 1630, described the houses of Turkish princes, which looked

> very artificially wrought both the foundation, sides and the roof of wickers ascending round to the top like a dove-coat; this they cover with white felt or white earth tempered with the powder of bones that it may shine the whiter, sometimes with black felt curiously painted with vines, trees, birds and beasts (Smith, 1630).

Thus one can follow the use of felt right up to the 19th and 20th centuries. The Cossack armies earned the name of "felt troops" because of the amount of felt they wore. As late as 1874, R. Shaw tells of a single caravan travelling the same year from Kashgar over the Terek Dawan to Khokand and consisting of 871 horse loads, including 120 loads of felt rugs, valued at 7000 Tungas, and 25 loads of Khotan carpets valued at 16,250 Tungas. (Bidder, 1964, pp. 37-9). This shows the relative value of the felt to the luxury carpet and yet the size of the load of felt gives further proof of its frequent use. In the Emirate of Bukhara, in the richest circles, felt wall-hangings were still used as late as the beginning of this century. A fine example was shown in the recent exhibition in Pittsburgh (Landreau, 1978). In fact there was not, up to the 19th century, any social distinction between the users of felt; it could be found in a palace or a *yurt* (circular felt-covered tent, also called *ak-ui* or *kirgha*). It was only in this century when so much of the ritualistic belief of the sophisticated classes was eroded by outside influences and modernisation, that felts became solely the fabric of the nomads — those who, from earliest times, have wandered back and forth over the steppes and other parts of Asia.

There is some evidence that the forbears of the Hungarians were responsible for bringing the art of felt-making from Central Asia to Europe. The Baskirs, a tribe which took part in the migrations westwards with the ancestors of the Hungarians, but settled on the way, in the region south of the Urals (Toynbee, 1973, p. 419), until recently had a strong tradition of making felt (Laszlo, 1944). In Hungary itself felt has long continued to be made; of particular interest is the garment called *szür,* "a long, straight-cut, coat-like garment" (Gervers-Molnár, 1973): made of felt, this is still worn by herdsmen of the great plains, the *Puszta,* while more prestigious examples of the *szür* are of woven cloth, highly embroidered. Linguistic evidence (Gervers-Molnár, 1973, pp. 21-4) indicates that the ancestors of the Hungarians adopted an earlier version of the *szür* from Turkic (cf. Hungarian *köpönyeg* and Ottoman Turkish *kepenek*) and Iranian (cf. Hungarian *köntös* and the Iranian word transcribed into Greek as *kandus*) tribes in the first millennium A.D. Presumably they also adopted the use of felt in general, for the Hungarian word for felt, *nemez,* can be compared with the Iranian *nemed* (and other Central Asian words for felt, e.g., Georgian *nabadi,* Khotanese *namadi,* "felt rug").

Chapter 4

FELT – MAGIC AND RITUAL

The vast territory where the nomads travelled was described by the Chinese in the 4th century B.C. as the "land of felt". This quiet admiration the Chinese had for the nomads is seen as late as 1763 when the authors of a handbook on the newly conquered provinces, Hsi-yü T'u-chi, made comments on the impressive absence of furniture. They described many details of the felts in use for sitting and reclining using the original Turki words. (Bidder, 1964, p. 34). Thus the nomads influenced their more sophisticated neighbours over a long period. There is no doubt that felt became firmly bound up with the nomads' thoughts and beliefs, their ceremonials, and religious lives, perhaps because originally it was of fundamental importance to the nomads' physical well-being.

Possibly the magical significance of felt may have resulted from some of the properties attributed to it. Krist asserted that when he was in Uzbekistan, scorpions never walked upon felt (Krist, 1938, p. 168). Von Schwarz, who travelled in Russian Turkestan, was told by the natives that "scorpions, phalanges, tarantulas, karakurts and snakes cannot move on felt mattresses" – and was never himself troubled when he slept on felt (Laufer, 1930, p. 13). Perhaps all creatures did not come under its spell, as L. Oliphant made this comment on his journey to the Tartar village of Bouyouk Yankoi:

> dismounting before a very low verandah, we entered a sort of hut by a hole about three feet square, and passing through a small room and another hole, found ourselves in a somewhat more spacious apartment, carpeted with thick white felt –

there were other rich trappings and towels –

> We were delighted with the comfortable air of the whole establishment – nothing could have looked cleaner than the white walls, or softer than the white felt; but we had not as yet experienced one property peculiar to the latter – the fleas had evidently been waiting until we were well in their power, and now transferred themselves in thousands from the felt to our bodies (Oliphant, 1853, pp. 221-2).

Very little evidence concerning the actual objects of devotion of the Asian nomad has come to light. Bidder quotes from a Chinese annalist:

> Tu-chueh (Turkish peoples) pay reverence to strange natural phenomena and magical powers, they have no ancestral tablets or temples. They cut out felt figures and put them in a leather bag . . . (Bidder, 1964, pp. 87-91).

In the third century A.D., although the Chinese ridiculed their nomadic neighbours because of their great dependence on felt, they recognised that felt was catching on in their own land:

> China has apparently been conquered by the nomads (Hu) for felt is a product of the nomads and now with felt fillets and girdles we adopt their styles.

This, in spite of the ridicule, was true, as there are ample references through the Han and T'ang periods to its frequent use for clothes and domestic purposes. But there is also reason to believe that they followed the nomads in using it for magic purposes, by cutting it up into human forms.

When Plano Carpini was Ambassador to the Great Khan of the Mongols in 1246, he described these idols of felt . . .

> They have certain idols made of felt in the image of a man and these they place on either side of the door of their dwelling, (cf. Chap. 2, p. 13) and above these they place things made of felt in the shape of teats, and these they believe to be the guardians of their flocks and that they insure them increase of milk and colts. Whenever they begin to eat or drink they first offer these idols a portion of their food or drink (Laufer, 1930, p. 15).

Friar William of Rubruck when he returned from his travels in Mongolia wrote:

> And over the head of the master is always an image of felt like a doll or statuette, which they call the brother of the master, another similar one is above the head of the mistress which they call the brother of the mistress, and they are attached to the wall. And higher up between the two of them is a little lark, one who is as it were, the guardian of the whole dwelling (Laufer, 1930, p. 15).

He remarked on another practice involving felt: a particular sect

> make images of their dead in felt, and dress them in the richest stuffs, and put them in one or two carts, and no-one dare touch these carts, which are under the care of their soothsayers (Olschki, 1949, p. 14).

Marco Polo described the god of the Tartars thus:

> They have a certain god of theirs called Natigay, and they say he is the god of the earth, who watches over their children, cattle and crops. They show him great worship and honour, and every man has a figure of him in his house, made of felt and cloth; and they also make in the same manner images of his wife and children. The wife they put in the left hand and the children in front. And when they eat, they take the fat of the meat and grease the god's mouth withal, as well as the mouths of his wife and children (Laufer, 1930, p. 16).

When Friar Odoric of Pordenone visited China between 1322-28, he described the minor Friars

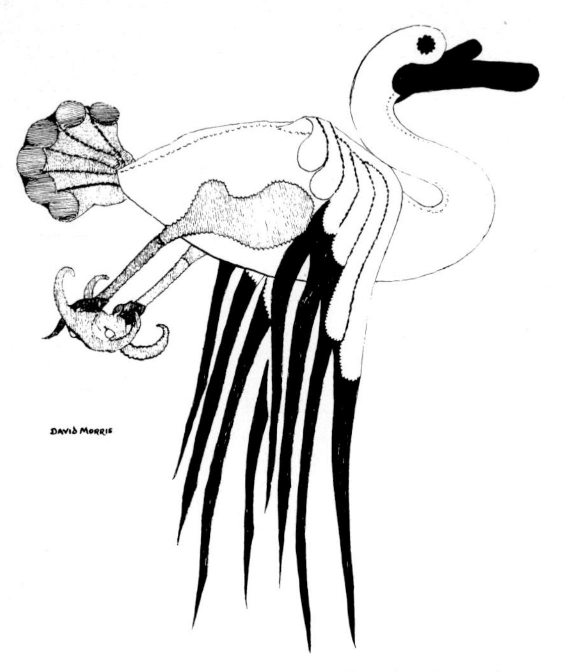

Fig. 8: One of four felt swans found at Pazyryk, Mound 5.

exorcising Mongol devils, when gods of felt were burnt in the fire.

Captain John Smith in 1630 described the Turkish princes thus:

> Having taken their houses from the carts, they place the master always towards the north, over whose head is always an image like a puppet, made of felt, which they call his brother; the women on his left hand and, over the chief mistress, her head; such another brother; and between them a little one, which is the Keeper of the house; at the good wives' beds-feet is a kid's skinne, stuffed with wooll, and neere it a puppet looking towards the maids; next the doore another, with a dried cow's udder for the women that milk the kine, because only the men milke mares; every morning, those images in their orders they besprinkle with that they drinks, bee it cossmos (kumis) or whatsoever, but all the while mare's milke is reserved for the prince. Then without the doore, thrice to the south, everyone bowing his knee in honour of the fire; then the like to the east, in honour of the aire; then to the west, in honour of the water; and lastly to the north in behalve of the dead (Smith; Laufer, 1930, p. 16).

There are a number of more recent felt idols in the Danish National Museum of Copenhagen, also in the British Museum, among the Sir Aurel Stein finds. It is perhaps possible that the four stuffed felt swans found at Pazyryk, which were probably to decorate the four corners of a cart, were not mere decoration but if not idols, had symbolic or magical powers (Fig. 8) and perhaps transported the Souls.

So much for felt as a form to be worshipped; what about its magical powers? It has been associated with many historic, ceremonial and ritual occasions. Persian Magi wore tall felt hats with side flaps extending down over cheeks and lips (Fig. 9) (Laufer, 1930, p. 10). Tibetan and Chinese kings were carried on white felt rugs into the presence of their audiences. The Mongols placed black felt inside their tents to keep out evil, and also used it in a practice noted by Carpini:

> when any one of them sickens unto death, a spear is put at his tent and around it they wrap a black felt; and thenceforth no-one who is a stranger dare enter the bounds of his dwelling.

The reason for this, explains Friar William of Rubruck, another traveller at that time, was their "fear lest an evil spirit or some wind should come with those who enter" (Olschki, 1949, p. 13).

Fig. 9: Headgear with earflaps, worn by a Chorasmian at Persepolis.

When Turkish tribes elected their chieftains, they used to raise them on a felt rug. In any description of ritual ceremony, to which they fervently adhered, felt rugs are mentioned long before any reference to woven examples (Bidder, 1964). The clearest and earliest account of the election of an emperor is contained in the Pei Shih, annals of the Northern Dynasties, where the election of the emperor of Northern China is described, according to the old custom of the Mongol nomads, whose territory the Chinese had conquered at that time (528 A.D.). During the election the emperor was lifted on a black felt by seven dignitaries. The felt here played a symbolic role, as the literal wording of the text shows – "the dignitaries *were covered by* a felt": this was a double consecration, in which the emperor made obeisance to heaven and was covered by it, just as the chief dignitaries made obeisance to their emperor under a felt, symbol of heaven (Olschki, 1949, pp. 27-34). This earliest text indicates the true significance of the felt, and contrasts interestingly with a medieval European account of the ceremony in 1206, which makes the felt very humble: Temuchin (who afterwards assumed the title Genghis Khan), was told to direct his eyes on the felt on which he sat, with the words,

> If thou wilt well govern thy kingdom, thou wilt rule gloriously, and the whole world wilt submit to thy sway, but if thou wilt do the reverse, thou wilt be unhappy and be outcast and become so indigent that thou wilt not even have a piece of felt on which to sit.

It is interesting to note further that this particular piece of felt was cherished as a relic for a long time to come (Laufer, 1930, pp. 14-15).

In all later accounts of the election of an emperor, it is stated that he was raised on a white felt. This disagreement over white and black felt may be due to the passage of time – white came to be revered in preference to black – or simply to the fact that different tribes are involved. There is abundant evidence that white felt was revered by the Mongolians — even up to when Laufer was writing (1930); placing a person on a white felt rug expresses good wishes for his welfare; a bride sits on white felt during the marriage cremony; an animal for sacrifice was slaughtered on white felt. The Türkmen also have a high regard for white felt.

Among the Mongols, women were usually responsible for making felt, which they called *dzulakhai* or *tolok,* rather than *ishighei,* which was not only a term of respect but had some magical connotation.

Chapter 5

MOTIFS AND DECORATION AND SOME POSSIBLE INTERPRETATIONS

Despite the present systematic research into carpet designs, much of the interpretation of motifs is speculative, but in considering felts from this wide range of ethnic groups from the Türkmen, Uzbek, Lakai, Kirghiz, Kazakh to the Qashqā'i, it is clear that important visual symbolic legacies of earlier cultures persist. David Lindahl's comment on Uzbek carpets also applies to felts, "patterns on Uzbek rugs reflect the process of geometricisation that takes place in many forms of art, whereby the details in a pattern, through constant use by a people with a common cultural heritage, can be excluded without undermining their essential meaning" (Lindahl and Knorr 1975, p. 20). Often motifs have become so stylised that they are unrecognisable to us, and now even to those who make them; I have had quite contrary explanations from felt-makers when questioned about individual motifs but they continue to be used repetitively, having become so deeply rooted, no doubt, as representing religious totemic emblems of magical traditions, dating in many cases from a pre-Islamic period. Their original figurative interpretation seems the more probable when one examines the evolution of figurative representations in early pottery in the same areas where, for example, animals rapidly became stylized in prehistoric times.

Pls. 17a, b: Two circular felt carpets at Bamiyan (from sketches).

Just as when considering the design of a knotted carpet, so it is important when considering a felt design to look first at its general composition. There are a number of ways a square or rectangular space can be subdivided. By using horizontal, vertical or diagonal lines one can create rectangles, squares or lozenges in which motifs may be placed. The oval and circle may also be used in felting, in a way impossible on a loom e.g. the round floor coverings of *yurts* in Afghanistan (Pl. 17a, b). In carpet designs the knotting technique dictates one set of conditions, in felting there are completely different possibilities. In carpet designs, however, there is a profusion of motifs and detail, too intricate to be achieved in felting except by embroidery. A smaller, simplified range of the motifs used on carpets appears on felts. However, the felt-maker often uses the general plan of a carpet design with a field and several borders. There are often simulated guard stripes made of twisted woollen lines laid between the main border and the field. Sometimes the guard stripes are filled with alternating coloured dots, suggesting a minor pattern. Although it is likely that the carpet designs are a sophisticated development of the original felts, in recent years there has been a two-way exchange of ideas.

Designs could be achieved in a number of ways, the following being the main methods:

(a) Motifs can be fulled into the felt during the process of felting, giving a mosaic effect.
(b) Decorations can be painted on when the felting process is completed. Sir A. Stein in his excavations in the Tarim Basin found fragments of painted felt (W. Meister, 1936). In more recent years of the 20th century, this practice has been re-introduced in Iran, Iraq, Turkey and Syria. (Cat. No. 18).
(c) Designs are created by superimposing one layer of coloured felt on another of a different colour and obtaining contrasts by cutouts, such as saw tooth edges. (Cat. No. 40).
(d) The motif can be appliquéd by using other pieces of felt, or cotton, silks, metallic strips, bark, leather or other material. (Pl. 15, 18).
(e) A mosaic pattern can be created by sewing small pieces of felt together with "antique seams" to hide the stitches joining them (Col. Pl. 8).
(f) Cord and silk bindings are used in a number of ways as borders or edges to either the motifs or the complete work. (Col. Pl. 8).
(g) Quilting is introduced as a means of reinforcing the material, usually in the form of zig-zag lines or spirals. Quilted straight lines could soon have led to the felt splitting, but the stitched spiral is an ideal means of joining the loose tufts of wool more surely. (Fig. 5, Cat. No. 39).
(h) Embroidery is used to produce figurative designs, ranging from flowers and animals to people. (Pl. 19, Cat. No. 37).

All these methods were known in ancient times and most can be seen in the Pazyryk felts. Meister, however, believed that method (a) first appeared in the wall paintings of the Tarim Basin from the Turfan Oasis, 8th-11th centuries A.D., where the Uigurian princes were represented as standing on felt carpet. However, finds at Çatal Hüyük would suggest the fulling of designs was already known in Turkey much earlier.

There seems to be a repertoire of motifs common to most felt-making groups.

Dots

The simplest pattern (used on the reverse of Türkmen rugs) is random dots in different colours on the natural ground (Pl. 20). Whether this could stem from a primitive type of design, or whether it is just the result of an Oriental desire to fill and decorate any empty space, is hard to say.

Lattice

The lattice pattern, (also used on the reverse of a mat, indicating that it is Türkmen) is used as a design and enclosed by a border (Pl. 21). Dots and lattice designs on the reverse bear no relation to the designs on the upper sides, neither in their construction nor in their patterns. Both these patterns are felted into the ground. Both dots and lines can, of course, be used as guide lines for designs in other instances (Pl. 3a, b).

Circle

Circles within circles are common motifs on plain or simply-bordered felts from Nuristan in Afghanistan (Cat. No. 36). They are usually applied by rough appliqué work in cotton superimposed on other material. They give the appearance of eyes and may have, according to some local tradition, warded off evil spirits. They recall those circular motifs used, one on either side of the shepherd's cloak, in Turkey (Pl. 22).

Triangle

If the general plan of the felt is subdivided into lozenges, triangles are formed at the inner edge of the border, and the border itself usually decorated by smaller triangles, either empty or enclosing other motifs (Cat. No. 44). These borders can further be

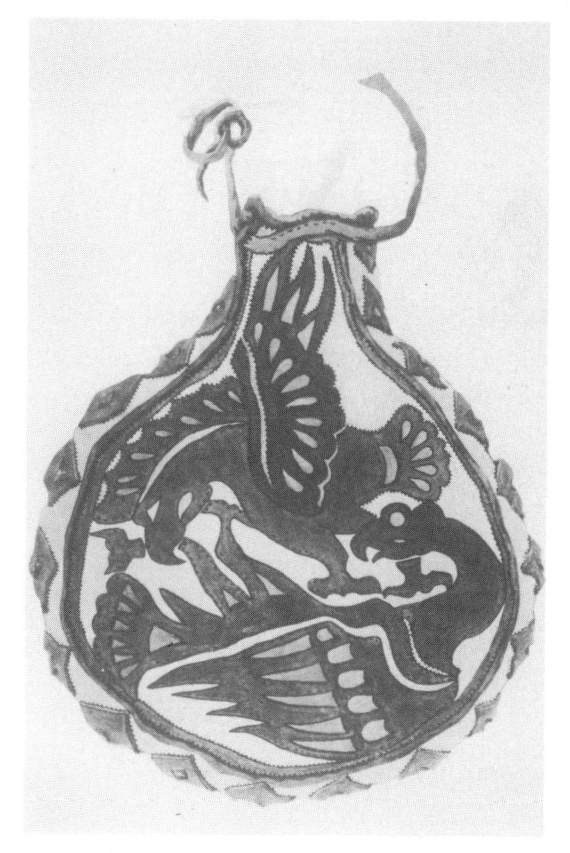

Pl. 18: Appliquéd leather flagon from Pazyryk, Mound 2.

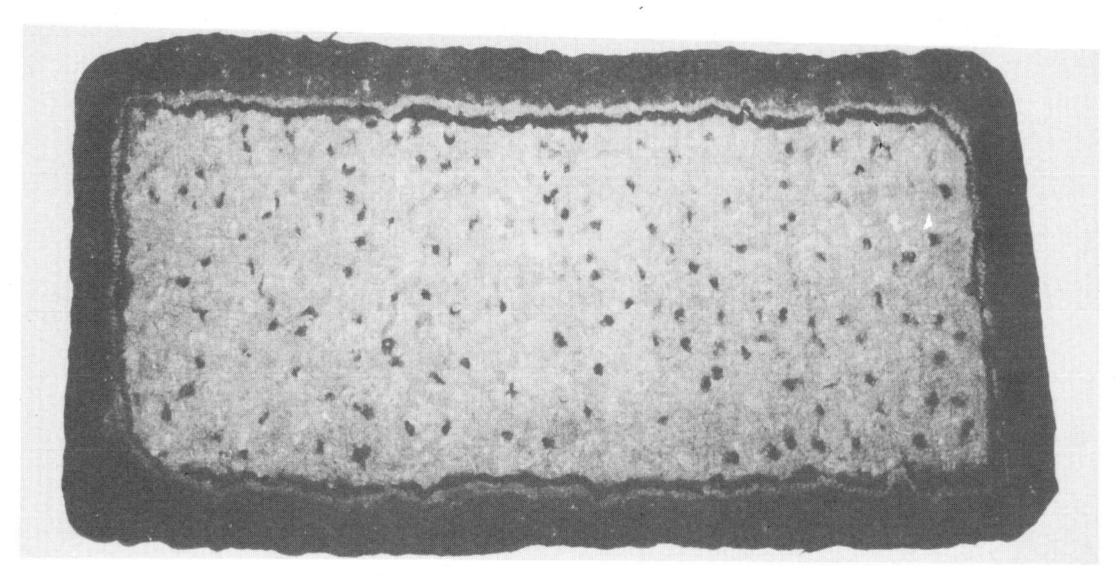

Pl. 20: Dots on reverse of Türkmen rug (Cat. No. 7).

◀ Pl. 19: A detail showing figurative drawing on a silk cover to a felt saddlecloth (Mound 5, Pazyryk).

decorated by a saw edge pattern of tiny triangles in reciprocal fashion, one colour felted next to another. This was already done at Pazyryk (Rudenko, 1970, Pl. 148). Triangular amulets are common in most parts of Asia and still worn by people and animals from India to Morocco, where donkeys and horses still wear them on their harnesses (Cat. No. 53). Many modern Afghan rugs from Ankhoi have layer upon layer of felt superimposed on each other, their edges forming a jagged saw tooth against the colour below (Cat. No. 40). Further triangular patterns can be achieved by using crosses and straight lines alternately along a border (Cat. No. 43).

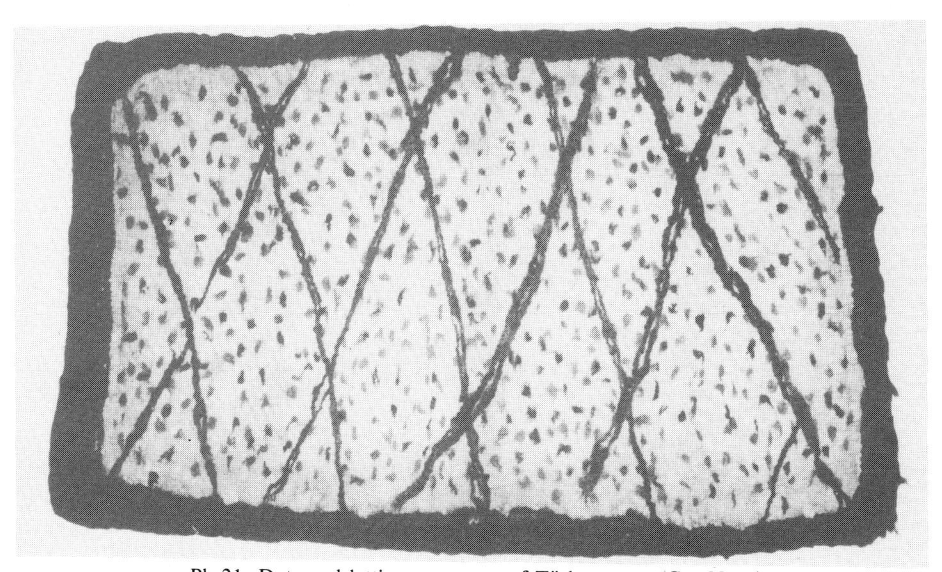

Pl. 21: Dots and lattice on reverse of Türkmen rug (Cat. No. 6).

Pl. 22: Man wearing *kepenek* in Konya.

Running Dog or Wave

The next most common device is the "running dog" or wave (Pl. 23). It is also known as the scroll, and scroll bands are common throughout the classical world in stone, mosaic, painting and other forms of decorative art. F. S. Meyer thought it was a purely geometric form (Meyer 1924, p. 151-2). But it could equally have derived from an animal motif, such as the stylised cockscombs which appear on some of the Pazyryk felts (Rudenko, 1970, p. 248). Bidder considers this latter motif might have been the forerunner of the so-called "lotus-tendril", and that in fact two separate lines of development, the Greek plant design and the Scythian or Turkish nomad animal design, may have become merged.

This motif repeated can be used as a border pattern and, used with two colours, divides a border equally into two reciprocal parts. The waves in one colour stand out against the opposing waves, producing a negative-positive design (Pl. 23). Bidder has pointed out how light and dark held magical significance in nomad ornamentation. Can this be seen as a symbol of the balance between the powers of good and evil – continual tension? He described how tribal princes were supposed to be descended from the "bright heaven, from the white cloud". After election to office they walked on white felt so as to avoid the dark ground (Bidder, 1964, pp. 87-91).

When looking at such a border, one is always aware of the motif nearest the lower edge of the border, the positive one, and only when viewing it from the opposite side does the other half of the pattern become the dominant one. It is rather like the old Chinese motif of the circle with a bit taken out – one cannot see them both properly in the same 'eyeful' – they have to be looked at separately (Fig. 10). The frequency of these negative-positive images in felt rugs is notable and I feel they dictate the way in which the rug should be seen.

Horn motifs

These are common in both felts and carpets. The goat's horn, so important in all nomadic groups, is known as *kochboynuzu* or *kojanak soynak.* Large goat or animal horns were used as decoration as early as the 3rd millenium B.C. on wheel-thrown pottery found at Ak-Depeh in Russia. Examples of the use of the frontal view of horned animals are numerous, many can be seen in Luristan bronzes from the 2nd-1st millenium B.C., as those in the Louvre, Paris (Pope, 1938, vol. IV, p. 34). Achaemenid jewellery, especially bracelets, shows horned animals as rhytons, vessel handles and earrings, as in examples at the British Museum, London (Pope, 1938, vol. IV, p. 122).

Horns themselves were of great importance in the lives of the various peoples of Asia for their usefulness in the making of artifacts, e.g. rhytons, drinking vessels and tools. The frequency of their appearance as decorative motifs testifies to this. When inverted and mirrored to form a more complex design, they are also known as *sekiz-ghochak,* i.e. eight scrolls (Beresneva, 1976, p. 7). This motif is mainly used amongst the tribes in Afghanistan. It is, however frequently found in Russia, Turkey and Iran, and Afghanistan (Cat. No. 47).

Pl. 23: Running dog or wave, or reciprocal volute patterns.

The sculpted rams' heads on the tombs of tribal heads of the Akkoyunlu, Karakoyunlu and Karakechili,* and also decorating doorways of houses, are numerous in eastern Turkey, for example, at Erzurum Museum and also Kars Cathedral (Fig. 11). Until recently pairs of horns were placed above doors of houses for good luck in Afghanistan (Pl. 24). Horn designs feature on kilim, pile and felt designs in eastern Turkey. After all, the whole economy depended on sheep and goats.

Tree of Life

This is a term used to describe a range of motifs supposedly representing a tree – but it must be noted that if a row of scrolls is inverted, this mirror image may resemble a tree. A tree pattern is often used in carpet design but that used in felts, quite often on door hangings (Cat. No. 5) or horse cloths, could equally well be rows of horns or, for that matter, volutes.

Fig. 10: Chinese circle.

The Spiral

The volute spiral very soon leads to complex spiral patterns and as these occur so frequently in the history of felt it may be worth spending some time considering them. In almost every prehistoric culture the spiral as a single structure appeared as a decorative motif. Its frequent occurrence on stone images, rocks, pottery and even upon the body extended from certain tribes of Australian aborigines, to Central America, the steppe lands of Central Asia and to the British Isles. Double spirals were carved by Megalithic man. This latter is the most familiar as the Yin Yang sign of the Far East. That man was at an early stage preoccupied with the spiral order and his own spiral development is obvious

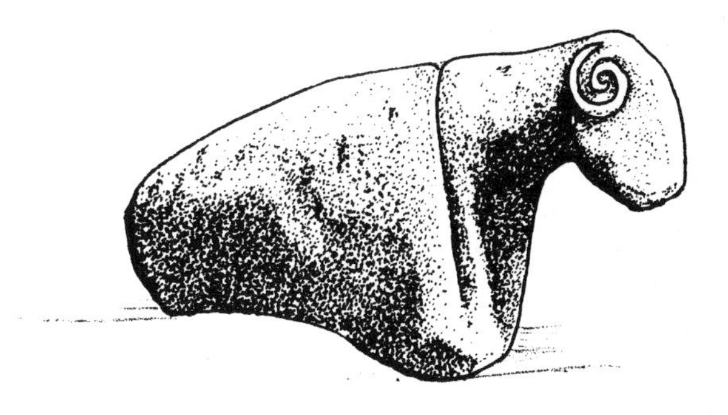

Fig. 11: Sculpted ram, tomb, Kars, *c.* 1100.

from the labyrinth of the nineteenth century B.C. in Egypt, Minoan Crete and Palaeolithic rock engraving.

Perhaps it is the most attractive single motif in nature to have aroused interest in early man in his search for a purely visual art form. It can, after all, be seen in shells from the simple snail to the more exotic forms of the sea and in the growth of plants and leaves. It can be seen in the spiral processes of wind, water, cloud and many other natural forces. The word "volute" comes from Latin (meaning "rolled"); "volute" in French means "snail shell". It can be seen on a Parthian sherd (Pope, 1938, vol. IV, p. 16). Double volutes decorate glazed brick revetments on the Achaemenid buildings at Persepolis and Susa.

Pl. 24: Goat's horns above a doorway in Afghanistan, 1977.

* Names meaning respectively, 'They of the White Sheep', 'They of the Black Sheep' and 'They of the Black Goats' (Abbot Hall Art Gallery, 1971, pp. 2-3).

Fig. 12: Spiral patterns on sand in Czechoslovakia.

Pl. 25: Reciprocal volutes.

In the spiral the early mystic discovered his symbol of eternity; it is certainly the most ancient symbol for this. Thus it ordered man's wanderings both before and after death in time and space. This two-dimensional version of the spiral, symbolic of the spherical vortex is first evident perhaps in ancient dance – the god Śiva – Sufi mystics – the dervishes – all revealed it in their movements, emulating the order of the cosmos. It was of great importance as the underlying principle of cosmic relationships themselves. The natural cycles of the yearly movement of the earth in relation to the sun form macrocosmic spirals in time. Taoist astrologers of ancient China founded their systems on these laws which are in direct correspondence with the ideas of Western astrology. The spiral contained the unifying principle of controlling the great opposing forces of differing polarities. Man himself has always understood that he is dominated by the forces of opposing solar and lunar currents – the forces of expansion and contraction – symbolized by wings and serpents (Purce, 1974).

In classical times certain ritualistic methods of spiral circumambulation were used in order to sanctify the ground in city construction. It is worth considering that there might be a link between this ritual custom and the simple spiral forms used in the design of the floor coverings of nomads' tents (Cat. No. 12). After all, they had to exist in the wide open spaces of Asian deserts and would have needed all the mystic protection they could achieve.

In much more recent times it is interesting to note the domestic use of spirals. Dr. Weyns, Director of Bokrijk Folk Museum, near Hasselt, Belgium, has written a study of the spiral patterns people used to make with white sand on the mud floors of Flemish houses. The housewife clutched a fistful and spread it (after cleaning and sweeping) like icing sugar on the borders of the floors (Weyns 1960). In Eastern Europe such sand patterns have been made until recent years (Czech Folk Art, 1975, p. 10) (Fig. 12). Could this Eastern European habit in recent folklore have come from further east and have any connection with the spiral patterns so common in felt floor coverings? (Pl. 23, 25).

It is perhaps a strange coincidence that the spiral, the main single motif employed in felt decorations, is in fact so closely related to the actual scientific process through which each single hair passes in becoming, along with all the other hairs, felt (Fig. 1).

The spiral is often used in felts as a means of stitching or quilting in order to strengthen the material (Fig. 5; Pl. 15). Camel covers in Afghanistan show stitched spirals and zigzags, or curving stitched lines used for this reason (Michaud, 1977, Pl. 20, 21). Could the origin of the spiral motif on felt have derived from its utilitarian purposes? Sir Aurel Stein found a fragment in Niya where red spirals had been cut out and appliquéd on to a yellowish ground. W. Meister in a reasoned analysis of the designs found on felts at Noin Ula in Mongolia, the Tarim Basin, Bezeklik and Shosoin, shows the use and re-use of this motif (Meister, 1936) over the period of 1000 years from 1st century A.D.

Chapter 6

FELT COATS

By VERONIKA GERVERS, Ph.D., Royal Ontario Museum, Toronto

Coats are the most characteristic of the many felt garments, exhibiting the greatest diversity in shape as well as in decoration. They provide protection for their wearers in lands of extreme climates, and serve as essential outer apparel. Innumerable variants of felt coats have survived into the twentieth century, although the manufacture of felt itself is definitely on the wane.

In addition to their practicality, coats often express the rank and social position of their owners, and are worn with great dignity and pride. This significance helped to preserve them.

Artistic depictions and written documents known from as early as the time of the Achaemenid Persian Empire attest that coats have had such symbolic meanings for a very long time in Western and Central Asia; this tradition must be much older. Whether made of felt or woven cloth, long coats were worn by kings, satraps, priests, and high-ranking dignitaries of the Persian court. On the stone reliefs of the Apadana of Persepolis, delegations coming from distant provinces of the Empire carry coats as special tribute to be given to Xerxes (486-465 B.C.). Those who presented these gifts are, nonetheless, never to be seen wearing such apparel. It seems reasonable therefore to assume that members of the delegations were forbidden to wear this prestigious outfit at least in the presence of their monarch.

The custom of wearing coats and presenting them to important personages on great state occasions was passed on to subsequent centuries. The 'robes of honour' of the medieval Arab courts would seem to derive from this very tradition. Presenting kaftans in the 'kaftan-giving hall' of the Ottoman sultans, and the offering of precious coats to important guests and their entourage in the courts of the emirs of Bukhara and Khiva vouch for the continuity of this age-old custom.

In spite of their relative simplicity, felt coats can also be associated with these ancient traditions. In Iran, for example, where most felt garments are made of sheep's wool and are now considered to be utilitarian garb for rural people, the felt coats of Qashqā'i chieftains (made of camel-hair or fine goat-hair) are looked upon with great pride, and are considered as status symbols. Their owners would rarely part with them no matter what their condition. The social significance of the beautifully embroidered white felt coats in eastern Iran, and especially in Afghanistan, is still more important than their practical aspect (Pl. 26, 27).

Due to the nature of the fabric, felt mantles are not necessarily cut from straight pieces of felt and then sewn together, as are coats made of woven cloth or pelts, but can be made in a single piece as though from a mould. Sewing is not essential to their construction, and many garments are made without using needle and thread at all. They have, nevertheless, some basic principles of construction which can be compared to, and more fully interpreted through, garments made either of skin or woven cloth. In the following pages, the construction of felt coats will be discussed in the light of these major traditions.

Pl. 26: Felt mantle with embroidered decoration, Afghanistan. Acquired in Kabul by the Third Danish Expedition into Central Asia.

SKIN TRADITION

The origins of felt can be closely associated with the life of pastoral nomads. The decoration of some felt rugs, and the construction of their ornaments can also be connected with skin and pelt mosaics, so characteristic of the art of hunting nomads in Siberia. Under the circumstances it is hardly surprising that the construction of certain felt coats can be linked to the cut of garments made of animal skins.

Typical in many areas of Iran and Afghanistan is a sleeved coat made from a square or rectangular felt blanket with minimal cutting and sewing, or no sewing at all. To form the garment, the blanket is folded in half vertically. Two horizontal cuts for the sleeves are made with slight angles about a third of the way down from the top, and a shorter vertical slit is cut down the centre for the upper part of the centre front opening. When the "cutting" of the coat is completed, the upper part is folded down horizontally to form the sleeves, and the sides below are turned in for the fronts of the garment. At this point, the sleeves and the horizontal front-seams are either sewn together, as in eastern Iran and Afghanistan (Pl. 26, 27) or, when the coat is made from a partially fulled felt blanket, as in Shiraz and Isfahan (Pl. 28-31), they are felted together. In the latter process, the cuts disappear entirely, and the neck opening, the cuffs and the hem-line may receive a fulled finishing which serves the same purpose as hemming does for garments made of woven cloth.

Pl. 27: Felt mantle with embroidered decoration. Pashtu. Badakhshan Province, Afghanistan.

Since, when felt is cut, the edges are seldom firm, and since the outer edges of a felt blanket are always quite uneven and loose, the centre front opening of these coats requires additional strengthening. The process can be achieved in various ways. In Shiraz and in the Isfahan area, the fronts of the coats are felted together during the fulling process (Pl. 29, 30), and a straight centre front opening is cut by scissors only when the garment is completely finished. In Shahreza (Iran), on the other hand, the front opening is sewn together prior to the fulling with tight and heavy stitches. When the coat is ready, this line of sewing is cut part way down, and the stitching provides a firm finishing.

This type of coat always has long sleeves which sometimes reach the hem-line, and can occasionally be even longer. New coats, especially when made in a professional workshop, are very stiff, and their sleeves cannot be used functionally. Thus the garments are worn over the shoulders with pendant sleeves. After some wear, however, the felt softens and the sleeves can become functional. In the Shiraz area, for example, villagers frequently wear the coats with their arms through the sleeves. In other places, as in villages near Isfahan, the sleeves are often made with closed ends, a definite indication that they are not intended for real use (Pl. 29). The same situation also occurs in parts of eastern Iran and in Afghanistan. There, the type of richly ornate felt coat has long, single flaps instead of proper sleeves, which serve precisely as decorative rather than functional elements. To enhance this effect, these vestigial sleeves are adorned with embroidery or elaborate cut-work (Pl. 26, 27).

Pl. 29: Felt coat with closed sleeves put out to dry on a roof top. Outskirts of Isfahan, Iran.

Pl. 28: Felt-maker showing a sleeved felt coat. Outskirts of Isfahan, Iran.

The construction of these coats with minimal cutting is reminiscent of that of garments from Siberia made of animal skin. The size of the blanket (*c.* 130×140 cm) from which these coats are made, and the position of the horizontal slits for the sleeves, correspond to the size and shape of a deer skin. This type of construction is not unique among skin and felt garments, but can also be distinguished among coats produced of woven cloth. Short jackets discovered in Denmark from the Bronze Age reflect the same tradition. The *guba,* a coat made of a heavy woollen fabric with flocks of wool twisted in during the weaving to imitate fur, is also made in this fashion. It was worn by Slavic groups of the Western Ukraine, Slovaks, Hungarians, and Romanians. The cut occurs among Polish jackets of the Zakopane region, made of fulled woollen twill. Occasional examples are also known throughout the rest of Europe.

Another type of felt mantle which may have its origins in a skin tradition is represented by those ample capes, called *burka,* which are known from the Caucasus as well as from West-Central Asia (Pl. 32). These capes are usually made of black goat-hair, and sometimes have a hairy surface to indicate that their predecessors were made of fur. A shorter *burka* of white goat-hair is usually worn by women. While the construction of the felt coats already described appears to have been characteristic over a very large area, these

Pl. 30: Fulling a sleeved felt coat. Workshop of Abdul Ali Ougi, Shiraz, Iran.

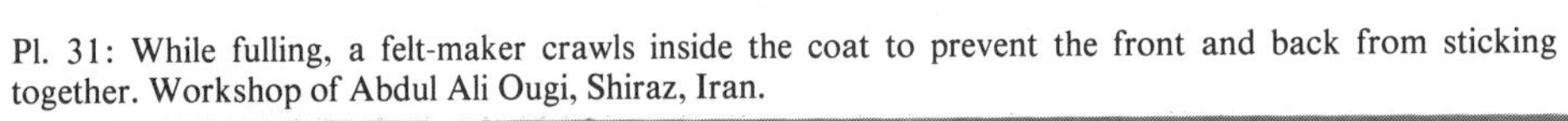

Pl. 31: While fulling, a felt-maker crawls inside the coat to prevent the front and back from sticking together. Workshop of Abdul Ali Ougi, Shiraz, Iran.

capes are less universal. The closest fur garments related to them are the large Hungarian shepherd cloaks or *subas* made of sheepskin, which may have reached the Carpathian Basin with the Hungarians at the end of the ninth century A.D.

CLOTH TRADITION

Since garments made of woven cloth were worn in most areas where felt is used, it is natural that they influenced the shape of felt coats. The construction of cloth garments is based on the width of the woven fabric, which is usually narrow in those parts of Asia where felt is made. This quality, however, made no impact on felt costume since felt can be made in any size and shape. Certain details of cloth garments, on the other hand, can be copied in another type of fabric, whence we can draw our conclusions.

In Central Asia, especially among Türkmen and Uzbek tribes, and the inhabitants of the great oasis cities, women wrapped themselves into large outer cloaks which covered them from head to foot. These cloaks had long vestigial sleeves tied together at the back. Though worn over the shoulders rather than over the head, related mantles are known to have been worn by the Ottoman Turks who spread the mode in the Middle Ages as far west as the Balkans. The non-functional tapered pendant sleeves of felt coats from Irani Kurdistan are often tied together at the back. Short slits are cut on either side of the upper front to enable the arms to pass through (Pl. 33, Col. Pl. 4a). So great is the similarity of this type of felt coat to those Central Asian garments previously mentioned that a direct influence cannot be dismissed.

Pl. 33: Felt coat (*qaput*). Seh Gabi (near Kangavar) Iran. Made by Mashd Heshmat Bakhtiari of Serkan in 1973; and supplementary diagram showing the construction of Iranian felt-coats. Below: Kurdish, Seh Gabi (after L. D. Levine, 1977); right: Shiraz.

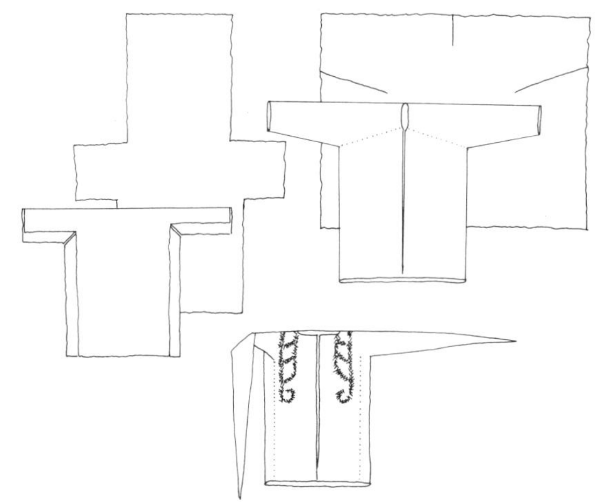

Pl. 32: Felt cape (*burka*). Tiflis, Caucasus.

Some Afghan coats with vestigial sleeves may also belong to the same general tradition. Their ornaments, including highly conventionalized embroidered flower sprays and rosettes in coloured wool, also suggest a close relationship with the embroidered decoration of women's coats made of silk or cotton fabrics, and worn over the head (Pl. 26, 27).

In addition to the Kurdish garments described above, other felt coats with pendant sleeves frequently have slits for the arms at the armpits. This style is well known from Persian court costume as well as from Ottoman Turkish kaftans, and simpler variants spread throughout Western Asia. Thus it is understandable that slits also occur on felt coats and jackets. In Iran, they are particularly widespread among the Kurds (Col. Pl. 4a). While in some cases these arm-holes are not real holes but simple slits, they are found in other examples to be bound with woven cloth.

Pl. 34: Tibetan village chief.

A FELT TRADITION?

The sleeveless Turkish *kepenek* mantles, which provide their owners with a cape as well as with a portable tent, represent a felt garment which may be unrelated to either the skin or the cloth traditions, but which was probably determined by the possibilities of its ground fabric (Pl. 36). The *kepenek* is made from a long, narrow blanket, the front half of which is narrower than that intended for the back of the garment. This blanket is then folded in half horizontally. The edges of the back are turned over the front, and felted together into a single item. In some places, as in Afyon, the bottom is also closed, and cut open only after the fulling process has been completed. At this time, a centre opening is slit down the front, and a small horizontal cut is made to form the neckline (Pl. 37-40).

The garment is extremely simple, and variety consists of making the shoulders broader or narrower, (depending on the traditions of the felt-manufacturing

Pl. 35: A *Hui-Hui* yak driver from Tibet.

Although vestigial sleeves must have existed on felt garments for a long, but as yet undetermined, period of time, arm-holes, embroidered ornaments, and perhaps the fastening of the sleeves at the back appear to be more recent developments. They may indicate the influence of Persian and Ottoman formal costume.

The costumes of Eastern and East-Central Asia must also have had an impact on the shape of felt garments. In Tibet, the overlapping front panels of felt coats indicate not only the practicality of such an overlap in the rough climate of the region, but recall the general tradition of cloth and skin garments which were all constructed with overlapping fronts. In these lands, it would obviously have been impossible to envisage felt garments without these basic coat characteristics (Pl. 34, 35).

centre involved, and to a lesser extent on the request of the person who commissioned the piece), and of cutting the front opening straight through the hem-line, or stopping at a distance of just a few centimetres above it, thus leaving the lower part of the garment to be held together by the hem. Decoration, if any, is scarce on the *kepenek*. The maker, however, often places his traditional sign, and marks the weight on the front panels by inlaying coloured felt pieces into the ground fabric. In recent times the old signs have frequently been replaced by the name of the maker (Cat. No. 65). The name of the person who ordered the garment may also be added on the inside of the coat.

Kepeneks have been worn by rural populations throughout Anatolia. Until recently, when the means of transportation improved, and bus services reached most far-away communities, these garments served for travellers too.

Closely related mantles are also known from North-Eastern Iran, especially from the Tabriz region. Some bell-shaped capes, worn in the Shiraz area, might also derive from the *kepenek*. While in Shiraz sleeved felt coats are the usual outer garments, these capes are specifically made against the precipitation of the winter months.

Kepenek mantles were usually worn with felt hoods, called *başlik,* in inclement weather. While high up on the dry Anatolian plateau hoods were only needed in the cold of the winter, the situation was rather different in Western Anatolia. Near the sea, precipitation is relatively frequent in season, and hoods are needed not only against snow but against rain. Thus in Balikesir and Tire, the best known felt-manufacturing centres of Western Turkey, the hood is made as an integral part of the *kepenek*. After the first hardening process, when the fabric of the mantle is more or less formed, and folded in half to be felted together, loose wool is spread for the hood. After the second hardening, the hood is shaped by fulling (Pl. 41-43).

In Turkey, the appearance of the hood as part of a *kepenek* is undoubtedly the result of a local development, and is entirely based upon the climatic conditions of the country. Similar occurrences of hooded coats, and coats worn with separate hoods, can

Pl. 36: Shepherds in *kepeneks* in the Afyon region of Turkey.

Pl. 37.

Pl. 38.

Pl. 39.

be observed among garments made of woven cloth in the Aegean and some Mediterranean islands, and the Balkans as well.

A construction related to that of the *kepenek* mantles is not uncommon among sleeved felt coats from Irani Kurdistan. In the villages near Kangavar, felt coats called *qaput* are also made from blankets which are folded in half to form the front and back of the garment. At the point where they are folded, that is to say at their shoulder line, they are generally extended with squares or rectangles to form sleeves. Some of these sleeves are short and open, though they are not intended for real use. The coat is worn over the shoulders as a cape (Col. Pl. 5a). In other cases, the sleeves of this type of coat are entirely non-functional. They are long, closed and occasionally tied together at the back. Even these sleeves, however, are made from those relatively small extensions of felt which are added to the shoulders, and which suggest that their predecessor lay in a short-sleeved coat (Pl. 33, Col. Pl. 5a). Short-sleeved coats are in fact made in the same area by the same craftsmen. Felt is a very versatile fabric, which can be made into almost any size and shape during the fulling process. The appearance of the final product thus does not necessarily indicate a single possible construction. Without seeing the manufacture of a felt garment, conclusions about its construction can only be considered hypothetical.

Sleeved garments similar to these Iranian examples might also have existed in Anatolia. In Tire, in 1973, an old felt-maker remembered that in his youth a sleeved and hooded *kepenek* was worn by shepherds when carrying milk; this was constructed in the same fashion as the coats described above (Pl. 41-43).

Thus, despite their differences and manifold types, felt coats probably derive from a few basic prototypes.

Pl. 40.

Select Bibliography on Felt Coats and Principles of Garment Construction

Burnham, Dorothy K., *Cut my Cote,* Toronto: Royal Ontario Museum (1973).

Gervers, Veronika, "A nomadic mantle in Europe", *Textile History,* **9** (1979).

"Construction of Türkmen coats", in Teheran (1978).

Gervers, Veronika and Michael, "Felt-making craftsmen of the Anatolian and Iranian plateaux". *Textile Museum Journal,* **4**: 1 (1974), pp. 14-29.

Gervers-Molnár, Veronika, *The Hungarian szür: An archaic mantle of Eurasian origin.* In the Series *History, Technology and Art* monograph 1. Toronto: Royal Ontario Museum (1973).

Levine, Louis D., "Notes on felt-making and the production of other textiles at Seh Gabi, a Kurdish village", in *Studies in textile history in memory of Harold B. Burnham,* ed. V. Gervers, Toronto: Royal Ontario Museum (1977), pp. 202-13.

Vollmer, John E., *In the Presence of the Dragon Throne: Ch'ing Dynasty costume (1644-1911) in the Royal Ontario Museum,* Toronto: Royal Ontario Museum (1977).

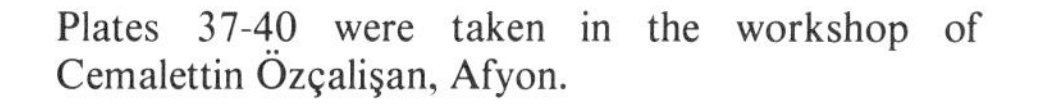

◄ Plates 37-40 were taken in the workshop of Cemalettin Özçalişan, Afyon.

Pl. 37: Carded wool is spread for a *kepenek.*

Pl. 38: The edges are folded and tied down after the first hardening.

Pl. 39: *Kepenek* numbered with red and blue felt strips after first hardening.

Pl. 40: *Kepenek* before fulling process.

Plates 41-43 were taken at the workshop of Mustafa Elal, Tire.

Pl. 41: Carded wool spread out for a sleeved *kepenek.*

Pl. 42: Before second hardening, carded wool is spread for hood.

Pl. 43: Front opening of sleeved *kepenek* cut with a knife after fulling.

Pl. 41.

Pl. 42.

Pl. 43.

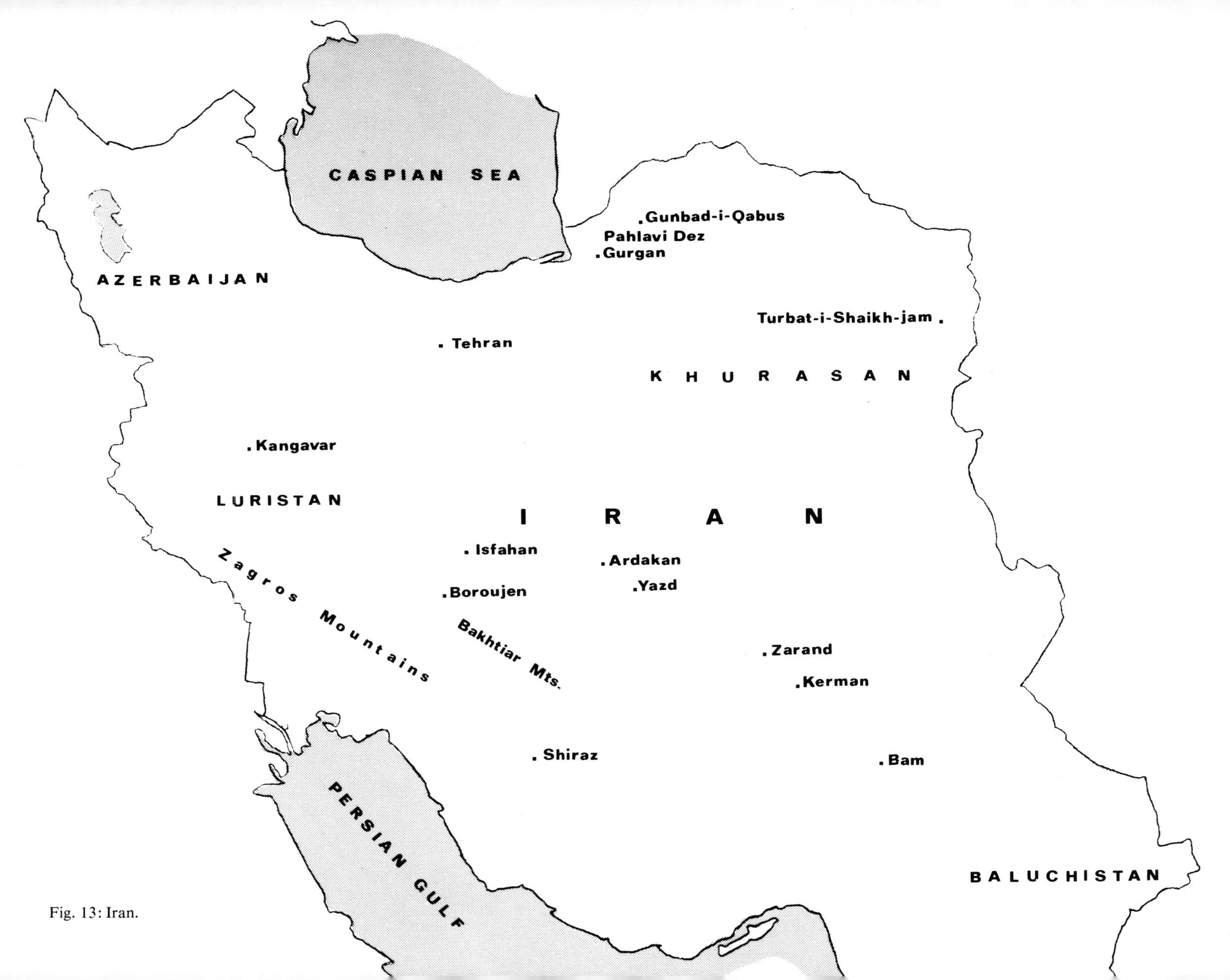
CASPIAN SEA
.Gunbad-i-Qabus
Pahlavi Dez
.Gurgan
AZERBAIJAN
Turbat-i-Shaikh-jam .
. Tehran
KHURASAN
. Kangavar
LURISTAN
IRAN
. Isfahan
. Ardakan
.Yazd
.Boroujen
Zagros Mountains
Bakhtiar Mts.
. Zarand
. Kerman
. Shiraz
. Bam
PERSIAN GULF
BALUCHISTAN

Fig. 13: Iran.

IRAN

Pl. 44: Feltmaking, Isfahan, *c.* 1890. Typical Isfahan carpet being smoothed by a roller.

In Iran the making of felt *namad*, has continued both in settled rural communities and amongst the nomads. When Ernst Höltzer (1835-1911) was in Isfahan he described the felt industries: "In the town (Isphahan) no carpets are made any more, but very good felt-carpets (Nemet) with simple white designs are still being made (Pl. 44). The Persians love these thick soft underfelts, particularly as runners or 'side-rugs'. Over these are put blue covers of cotton in order to sit on a cool surface in the Summer and also to keep the Felt clean". He said that 30 Nemädmal – makers of felt-covers – still worked in the town (Höltzer, unpub.). There are further descriptions of felt-making in Isfahan in 1894 by J. R. Preece in the Consular Reports for that year. He mentioned horse cloths and saddles, felt coats "large and roomy, with arms", the staple article used by the Persian peasant as a protection against the great cold he had to encounter during winter in and about Isfahan. He also mentioned felt hats, "generally used by all sorts and conditions of people. They are of various forms and shapes. Tell a Persian what style of hat a man wears and he will be able to tell you whence he comes or to what tribe he belongs" (Preece, 1894, pp. 21, 49). He said a good felt would take five days to make. He also reported felt-making in Yazd: "Yazd used to do a large trade in felts *namads* which were used mainly for carpeting the rooms on the sides and top. Two pieces of equal length and of a similar pattern, about 40 inches wide and from 3 to 6 yards long and some 1 to 2 inches in thickness were put down each side of the room touching the walls. A cross piece of the breadth of the room and $2\frac{1}{2}$ yards deep was placed at the top of the room and the centre between them would be filled in with a good carpet. The host would sit in a corner on the top felt, and the guests would range themselves according to their rank, right and left of him

Pl. 45: *Yurts* near Gunbad-i-Qabus. 1962.

down the room. Now, owing to the advancement of European ideas and a desire to have the whole room covered by one carpet, this industry has largely decreased. In Yazd, fine and beautiful *namads* are still made, sometimes of enormous size, sufficient to cover entirely a large hall. These are usually mostly made for the notables in Tehran" (Preece 1894, pp. 21, 49). Other references include the felt-making of Kerman esteemed to be the centre of the best felts both for softness and hard wearing. The designs on Kerman pieces were described as prettier and more colourful than those in other towns where colours were limited to white and red. He referred to the widespread making of felt and apart from the most notable centres of it (Yazd, Isfahan and Kerman), found that the village of Zarand, 80 miles to the North-west of Kerman, "had the reputation of making the best felts in Persia." (Preece, 1894, p. 32). Major B. Lovett described one which came into his possession at Bam, "covered with an intricate geometrical pattern in blue and green worsted . . . In an inner room carefully protected from the wind, is a polished plaster platform. On this pieces of coloured worsted are arranged in the designed pattern, with some sort of size. A very thin felt is then carefully pressed over them, and at once removed, carrying on its face the pieces of worsted in their proper places. This thin felt is laid on the thicker felt of the carpet and the two incorporated with blows of a mallet" (Goldsmid, 1876, Vol. I, pp. 101-2). No doubt the inclusion of some worsted gave the felt extra strength. Similar use of woven material was found at Gordion in Turkey (Bellinger, 1962).

The main centres to have continued the tradition of felt-making are in the North-east of Iran, among the Türkmen around Gurgan, Pahlavi Dez and Gunbad-i-Qabus, and in the south where the Bakhtiar and Qashqā'i migrations take place. The northern plains and surrounding mountains still provide much grazing despite reclamation of land for other purposes under recent development policies. The Türkmen are descendants of the Oghuz Turks who migrated west from Mongolia in the 10th century and number twenty-two sub-groups. Of these there are the Salor, Tekke, Yomut, Saryk, Atabay, Chaudor and Ersari, who, though orthodox Sunnis still show relics of pre-Islamic shamanism and independence. (For example, though living in Iran, they do not use the veil, but brightly coloured scarves of their own designs). The Atabay Yomut near Gunbad-i-Qabus (Pl. 45) are the makers of perhaps the best contemporary felt, both interesting in design and very robust in quality.

Although there has been such a tradition of felt-making in Northern Iran, it is rapidly changing. The Türkmen are reported as saying that in five years' time all felt will probably have disappeared from all the new sedentary settlements and urban communities. The women find the hard rolling with their bare forearms hurts their arms and they are less and less inclined to do it (Pl. 2). Of course they do use the other method for rolling some stages of the process (Pl. 46). Besides, both settled and nomadic Türkmen are now well able to afford more luxurious woven carpets to replace the felts. Some when settled, however, have kept their felts as heirlooms in memory of former days (Pl. 47). It has thus been possible to acquire pieces no longer made, such as the hearth felt (Cat. No. 11). Only two of these are believed to exist in the Obah area near Gunbad-i-Qabus.*

Türkmen designs are not only some of the most satisfying but the most traditional. Most of them bear the simple spiral motif in various forms and arrangements. The best of them are done in red, brown, ivory and black on natural brown or ivory bases. They are nearly always double-face; that is the base is planned with its own simple design of lattice or dots on the reverse side, while the upper surface bears the main motif (Pls. 20 and 21).

Near Shiraz in the south there are several centres of felt-making, Ardakan, Semirom and Boroujen being the most important now. It is occasionally made by the tribal women but more often by non-tribal villagers who exchange it with the tribesmen for wool. They have one clipping a year, washing the sheep just prior to the clip, not using soap. The quality of the wool varies according to the age of the animal, the younger producing the finer. The best wool taken from the rear

* I am grateful to Henrietta Moore and Virginia Allon who went to Gunbad-i-Qabus and collected material for the exhibition on my behalf, with the help of Abdul Khadjeh.

Pl. 46: Women rolling felt with cord. Gunbad-i-Qabus. 1962.

underside of the animal is used for the shepherd's cloak, *kapanak,* (Cat. Nos. 27 and 28), and the rest for floor felts. After the rolling, the Qashqā'i full the felt, at which stage the loosely felted blankets intended for cloaks are pulled into shape (See Chap. 6).

The goat produces two layers of wool, an upper hair and lower *kolk* which is used for hats, *bork,* worn by headmen, *Khans,* and other rich members of the tribe. Nowadays the measurement of the wool by weight is done under the metric system whereas previously it used to be per fleece. Felt for hats has to be pressed into a metal dish, c. 1 m in diameter by one man using his hands and feet (Pl. 48; Col. Pl. 5b). According to skill and the quality of the wool, a team of four in the bazaar at Shiraz take one day to make ten hats. One prepares the wool, another presses it, while a third places the prepared felt on to a wooden mould, smoothing it with a polished stone (cf. Pl. 44) and the fourth cuts and finishes the material. These felt hats are always made by men who usually leave them out in the sun to dry (Pl. 49).

Unlike the guilds of felt-makers in Turkey, in Iran it is more usual for families to make it for their neighbours and themselves. As recently as 1974 it is reported by Dr. L. D. Levine that a felt-maker, Heshmat, will supply the needs of people in Serkan near Kangavar, visiting people in their homes, using their own wool, making the felt and moving on (M. & V. Gervers, 1974, p. 25).

There are no Qashqā'i embroidered felts, and the Qashqā'i are no longer making their own felts as formerly. They are not so ambitious as the Türkmen, and their need for felt is much less because of the milder climate in the south. The range of felts made included: shepherd's coat *kapanak,* hat *bork,* shepherd's socks *charouq,* waterpipe bags *ghaly'an-dan,* undersaddle felt for (a) horse *araq-gir,* (b) camel *alouq,* (c) donkey *patan.*

Pl. 49: Hats drying in the sun.

Pl. 47: Homes of recently settled nomads, where felts are still being used. Gunbad-i-Qabus. 1970.

Pl. 48: Felt hat-maker's workshop. Isfahan. 1966.

In the last few years the quality of the work has declined for various reasons. In Shiraz, however, Bahman-Begi has been fostering tribal crafts, including felting, in his government-sponsored school in recent years. Other tribes (Lurs and Bakhtiars) are unfortunately emulating the designs of the Qashqā'i, so tending to lose their own tribal traditions.

There is also a decline in the quality of the actual felts in Southern Iran, because the new tourist markets are satisfied with cheaper products. Now many tribal women are moving to towns where their labour has become marketable and they earn more, and are therefore abandoning tribal activities. Finally, patterns can now be block-printed on to the felt, which is a degenerate but time-saving method recently re-introduced. The effect is unsatisfactory as the pattern is less well defined and wears off quickly. The most modern introduction in Iran is a mass produced felt, part woven, edged with rubberized cotton binding and dyed lightly. These are sold in Tehran for the tourists and are more expensive than the real articles (Cat. No. 18 and 19).

A little felt is made in Luristan and Bakhtiar country, and felt coats and rugs are made by the Baluch, while the Teymouri to the east, south of Turbat-i-Shaikh-Jam, make felt mats and coats (Pl. 50).

Pl. 50: Two boys wearing *kepeneks* at Karat. Iran. 1966.

Sāmiabād, a village 32 Kms north-east of Turbat, and close to the Afghan border, has a population of 500 Iranians but includes a few Türkmen. There are large herds of Baluch sheep whose wool is used in the late autumn for felt making. The mats, c.1.5 × 2.5 metres, resemble in strength of colour Türkmen examples, but in types of design those of Afghanistan, rather than of the Qashqā'i.

All the members of the family help and each *namad* takes about four hours to make, including an initial stage of one hour's rolling, a drying period and a final two hour stage. They now use plastic sacking for the initial stage. After the design is laid down in dyed unspun wool, a thick layer of natural white wool is spread, to the required size, over this. Hot water, and nowadays a little detergent to act as a cleaning agent, are sprinkled on top before rolling (Pl. J i-iii). In fifteen minutes it is unrolled and edges and corners straightened before re-rolling for five more minutes. The process is repeated several times, finally turning the mat design uppermost so as to adjust it more easily, and discarding the sacking (back cover). The men do the heavy work here, and hang the mat on the wall for an hour to dry, while the rest of the family start on another. Then the men roll the mat for its final felting process for a further two hours, dry it on the wall and it is ready to use.

I am indebted to Dr. Shirley Jarman for the above information obtained while working in Eastern Iran in 1978, and she has kindly allowed us to use four of her photographs (Pl. J i-iii, back cover).

Pl. J i. Detergent sprinkled over wetted wool.

Pl. J ii. Prepared wool being carefully rolled up on sacking base.

Pl. J iii. Roll is bound with goat hair.

1 Felt Fragment *c.* 586 A.D.
Max. length, 54 cms, max. width 47 cms. Shahr-i-Qūmis, Iran. This fragment of felt was found by John Hansman in excavation of the Parthian site of Qūmis, identified by him as Parthian Komish, and later as a Sasanian town. The felt can be dated approximately by its association with a Sasanian coin of the 7th year of the reign of Hormizd IV, 586 A.D.

Restored by Miss J. Glover, North Western Museum and Art Gallery Service, Blackburn.
(Hansman and Stronach, 1970, p. 148).

Cat. No. 2.

2 Cradle Felt (*Salincak keçesi*). *c.* 1950.
110×57 cms. Yomut. Near Gunbad-i-Qabus.
Double face, wool. FACE: Natural ivory field, divided into two squares, each containing four spirals in black, edged with red, and a central roundel; surrounded by guard stripes of red and maroon, enclosing dots; an outer border of brown. REVERSE: Natural ivory field, overlaid with irregular lattice of red, dark blue and black stripes, and random dots in similar colours; enclosed by red stripe; outer border of brown.

The two ends of the felt are folded round ropes suspended from the lattice wall of the tent, upper face showing. This felt was a family heirloom, among the last traditional cradle felts to be made. (See also No. 3.)

3 Cradle Felt (*Salincak keçesi*). *c.* 1930.
107×57 cms. Yomut. Near Gunbad-i-Qabus.
Double face, wool. FACE: Red field divided into two squares, each containing black spirals in the corners, linked along the sides by a comb pattern, edged with maroon; a flower in the centre; surrounded by black and red guard stripes, and contained within a brown border. REVERSE: Natural brown ground, divided into field and border by stripes of red and black; two panels contain *Tirana* motifs and rosettes and dots in red, black and ivory.

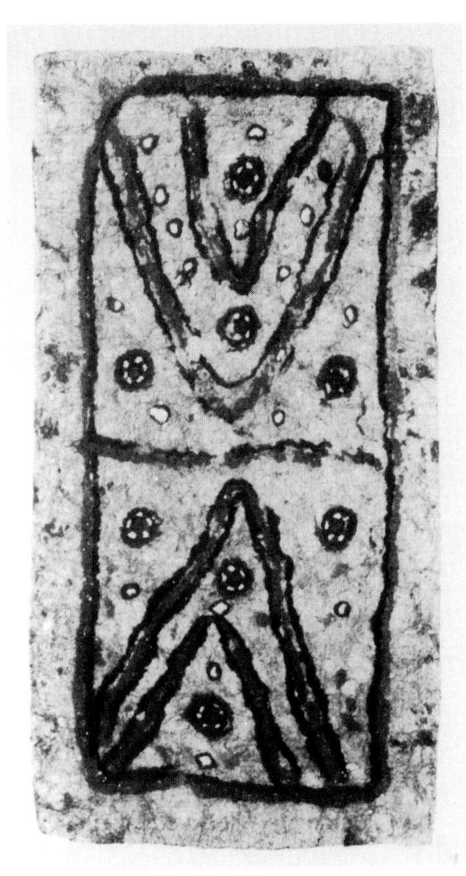

Cat. No. 3 Reverse.

4 Prayer Mat *(Namāźlik)*. 1973.
152×95 cms. Yomut. Near Gunbad-i-Qabus.
Single face, wool. FACE: Natural grey ground, overlaid with linear pattern imitating traditional form of lambskin, in red and black, including three "S" or *Kamcha* motifs.

This felt is partly machine-processed. The "S" motifs are probably intended (as in Turkish examples) to ward off the evil eye.

Col. Pl. 1: Horseman from the great felt, Pazyryk, Mound 5.

Col. Pls. 2 and 3: Floor felts from Gunbad-i-Qabus.

Col. Pl. 4b: *Kepeneks* at Bozyiğit Köyü, Turkey. 1978.

Col. Pl. 4a: Kurdish shepherds in felt coats. Kangavar area, Iran.

Col. Pl. 5a: Arab Ali, a Kurdish villager in a short-sleeved felt coat. Seh Gabi (near Kangavar), Iran.

Col. Pl. 5b: Felt hat-maker's workshop. Shiraz. 1966.

Col. Pl. 6: Floor felt from Kunduz.

Col. Pl. 7: Uzbek rug from Kunduz.

Col. Pl. 8: Quilted felt 1970, showing appliqué, antique seam, Kazakhstan

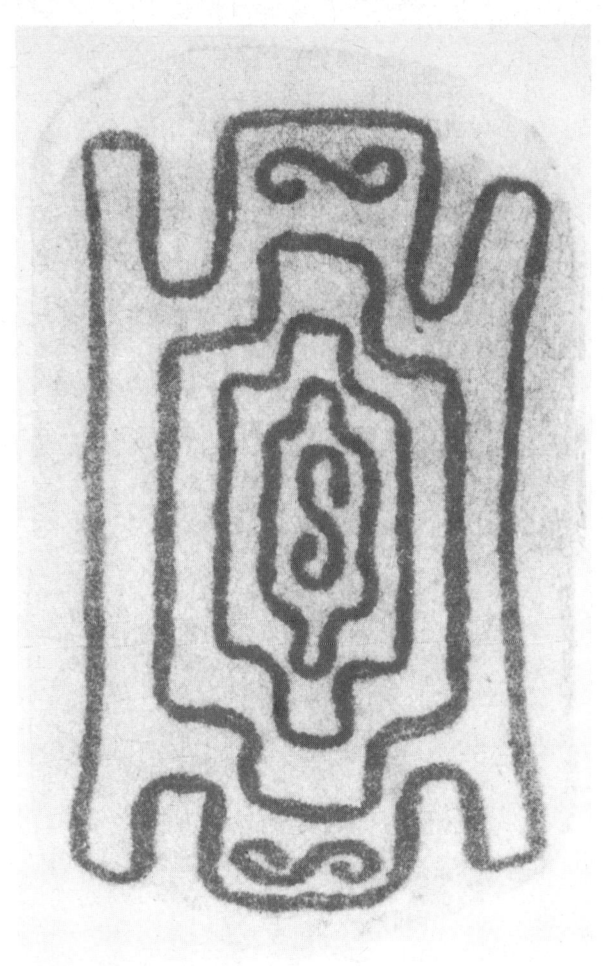

Cat. No. 4.

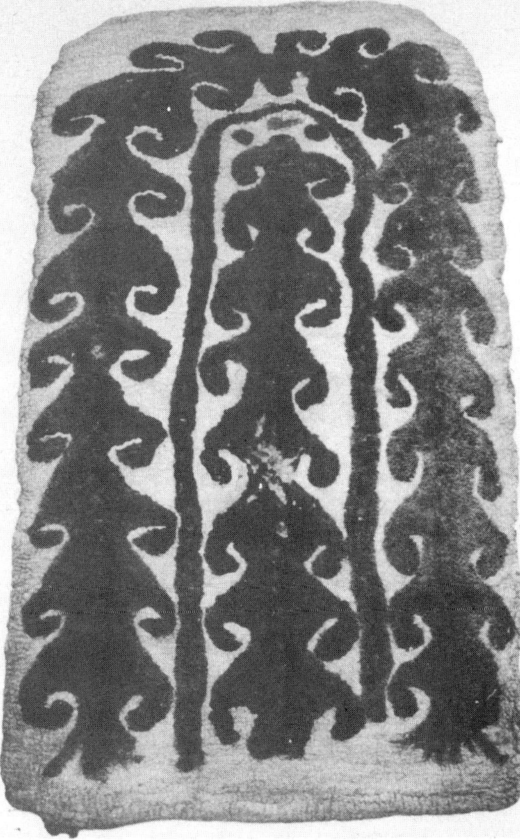

Cat. No. 5.

5 Door/Horse Felt *c.* 1925.
164 × 100 cms. Jafferbay. Near Gunbad-i-Qabus.
Single face, wool. FACE: Natural ivory ground with central "tree of life" pattern in red, edged with black, with alternating black "branches" in an arch flanked by a similar pattern, meeting at the top; a guard stripe of black and maroon enclosing dots forms the trunk and the arch separates the two.

Possibly a door felt adapted for use as a horse blanket. The rounded end would extend as far as the horse's tail. Similar "tree of life" designs appear in knotted pile saddlecloths *shabracks*.

6 Floor Felt (*Keçe*). *c.* 1930.
172×110 cms. Yomut. Gunbad-i-Qabus.
Double face, wool. FACE: Field of natural ivory; segment of a lattice pattern; enclosed by black and red guard stripe; next, a reciprocal pattern of black and red, with pink line between; guard stripe; brown outer border. REVERSE: Natural wavy field, with lattice pattern in maroon and blue-black, with red and blue-black dots. Red and black guard stripe; brown outer border. (Pl. 21) (Among vegetable dyes, pink is now rare).

7 Floor Felt (*Keçe*). *c.* 1950.
162×103 cms. Yomut. Near Gunbad-i-Qabus.
Double face, wool. FACE: Natural ivory field divided into two squares, each containing grey spirals at the corners, edged with red, joined along sides by comb pattern in similar colours, and a curvilinear swastika in the centre; red guard stripes enclosing dots surround the field; a border of reciprocal volutes in red, and grey and green alternately; grey and red guard stripes; brown outer border. REVERSE: Light brown field, dotted with red, green, maroon, blue-black; irregular guard stripes in red and black; brown outer border. (Pl. 20)

Green is difficult to produce with vegetable dye, and is now rarely used.

8 Floor Felt (*Keçe*). *c.* 1925.
192×97 cms. Yomut. Near Gunbad-i-Qabus.
Double face, wool. FACE: Field consisting of a natural ivory ground, divided into three squares; each containing at the corners, pink spirals, edged with black on the outer sides, and joined by undulating lines, and a roundel in the centre. Surrounded by narrow pair of maroon guard stripes, enclosing dots; next a reciprocal pattern in black, edged with maroon, and pink; a black guard stripe; outer border in brown. REVERSE: Natural light brown ground, spotted with maroon, red, pink and black, enclosed by irregular pink and black guard stripes; outer border of brown.

Cat. No. 6.

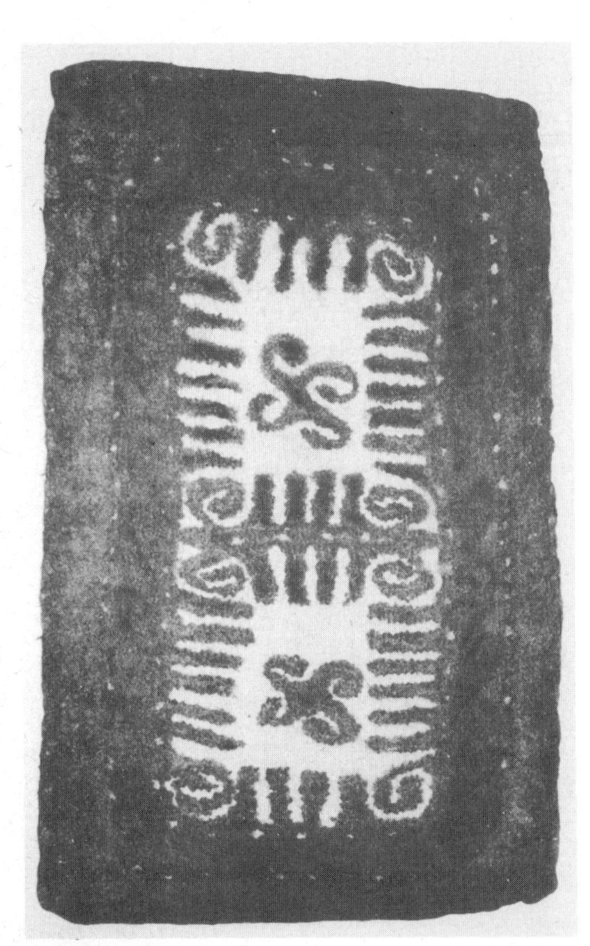

Cat. No. 7.

Cat. No. 8.

Cat. No. 9.

9 Floor Felt (*Keçe*). *c.* 1940.
155×96 cms. Yomut. Gunbad-i-Qabus.
Double face, wool. FACE: Field of natural ivory; small segment of a lattice pattern, each space containing a small roundel and spirals in blue-black, edged with red; red and blue-black guard stripes, enclosing dots; spirals enclosed by further guard stripes enclosing dots; outer border of brown. REVERSE: Natural ivory field, enclosed and divided by guard stripes of red and blue-black; a border of reciprocal volutes, blue-black edged with red, on ivory; red and blue-black guard stripe; brown border. The patterns on both sides normally occur as face patterns.

10 Floor Felt (*Keçe*). *c.* 1960.
211×119 cms. Yomut. Gunbad-i-Qabus.
Double face, wool. FACE: Red field divided into three squares each containing spirals at corners linked by comb pattern, and enclosing a curvilinear swastika in maroon and black. Two pairs of guard stripes enclosing reciprocal volutes. Outer dark brown border. REVERSE: Field entirely covered by volutes in red and black on natural and surrounded by reciprocal volutes and outer dark brown border.

Cat. No. 9 Reverse.

Cat. No. 11.

11 Hearth Felt (*Ocāq Başí Keçesi*). 1930.
351×213 cms. Yomut. Near Gunbad-i-Qabus.
Double face, wool. FACE: Mottled light brown ground, made up of three pieces from one original length; decorated in pink, black, maroon and ivory with reciprocal volutes ("running hound" pattern), "tree of life" inverted scroll pattern and *Tirana* patterns; edged at fire end with plaits. REVERSE: Stars, lines and dots on light brown ground.
One of only two left in the district.

12 Large Felt (*Keçe*). *c*. 1925.
313×188 cms. Yomut. Gunbad-i-Qabus.
Double face, wool. FACE: Field divided into five pairs of rectangles, each containing a spiral medallion and corner spirals connected by undulating lines. Border containing pairs of alternately reversed spirals. Outer brown border. REVERSE: Light brown natural ground divided into four large and four small partitions by red and black lines enclosing dots, which contain spirals in red and blue-black. Reciprocal spiral border and plain outer border.

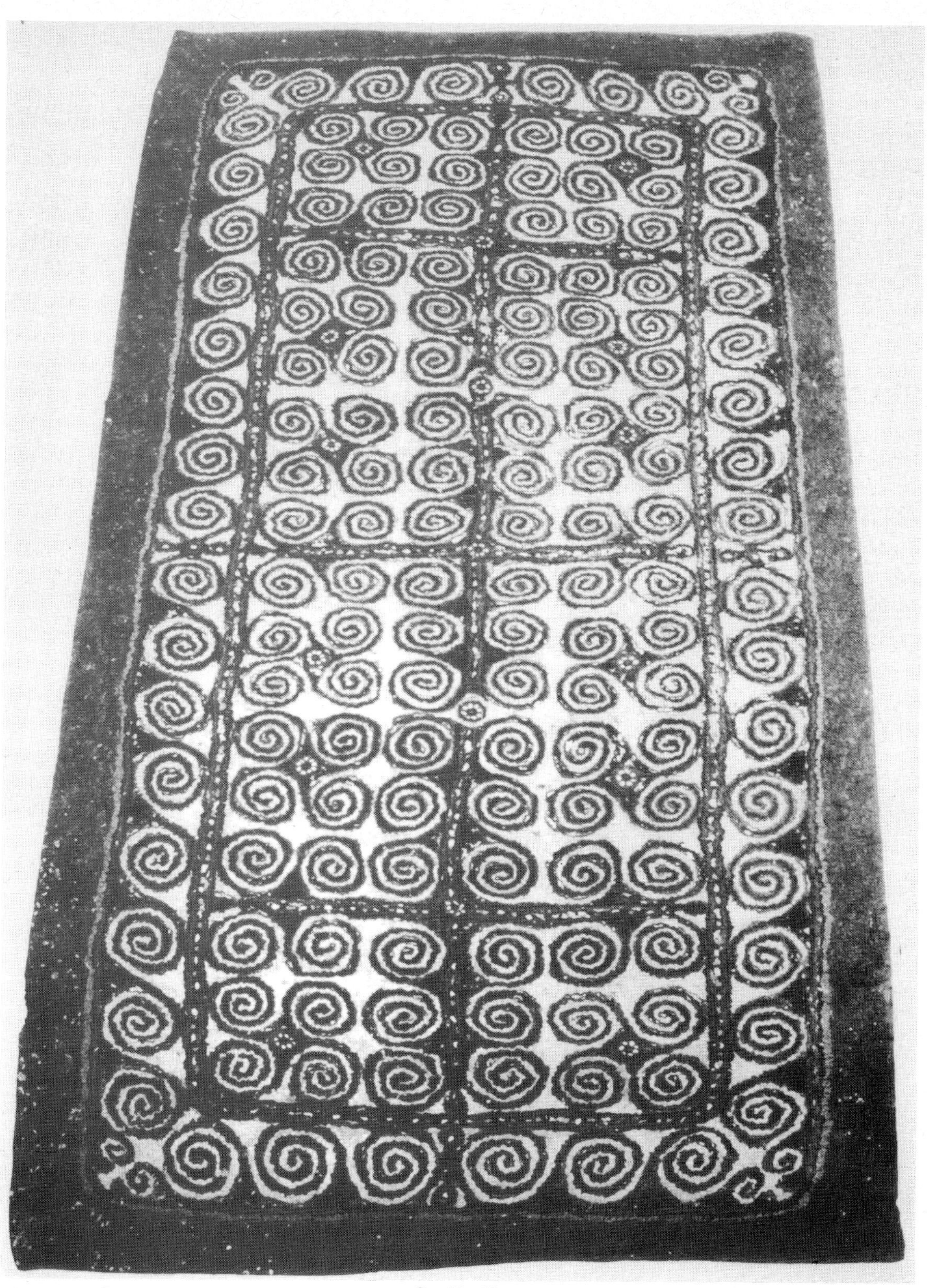

Cat. No. 12.

Cat. No. 13.

Cat. No. 13 Reverse.

Cat. No. 14.

13 Floor Felt (*Keçe*). *c.* 1945.
148×97 cms. Yomut. Near Gunbad-i-Qabus.
Double face, wool. FACE: Light brown field in two panels, with *Tirana* motifs in red, black and maroon, surrounded by guard stripes of same colours; brown outer border. REVERSE: Light brown field, overlaid with irregular lattice and random dots of black and red, enclosed by red stripe; outer border brown. Both patterns normally reverse.

14 Floor Felt (*Keçe*). 1950.
168×96 cms. Yomut. Gunbad-i-Qabus.
Double face, wool. FACE: Two central medallions with circular volute patterns, mottled brown and dark blue spirals, surrounded by reciprocal volutes ("running hound" pattern) and spiral hooks and dotted lines. REVERSE: Lattice pattern in three shades of red on light brown ground. Brown border and guard stripe.

15 Donkey Saddle Felt. 1968.
104×94·5 cms. Yomut. Gurgan.
Single face, wool. FACE: Natural beige ground with small central saw-edged medallion enclosing two flowers and surrounded by two patterned borders, in brown, red, yellow and grey.

Cat. No. 17(a) and (b).

16 Model Felt Tent 1978.
70 cms. diam.
This model, to the scale of 1:8, and not claiming to be exact in every detail, shows the use of felt in a Yomut *yurt* (properly called an *öy*). The structural principles of the *yurt* are the same wherever it occurs, in a belt 1,000 miles from north to south and stretching a quarter of the way round the world.

Made by C. L. Randall, from details supplied in an article by P. A. Andrews (Andrews, 1973).

17a & b. Pot Holders (*Tutaç*). *c.* 1966.
19×15 cms. Atabay Yomut.
Two triangles of felt with red, green and blue sewn edges and spiral pattern on upper faces; woollen tassels and connecting plaited cord.

Cat. No. 18.

18 Felt Mat (*Keçe*). 1978.
109 cms diam. Tehran.
Single face, wool. FACE: Natural beige ground. Circular mat with central motif printed in pink, maroon, orange, green and blue with a fish-bone patterned border; surrounded by triangles capped with flower emblems, edged with black binding.

19 Felt Mat (*Keçe*). 1978.
200×137 cms. Tehran.
Single face, wool. FACE: Natural beige ground. Field consisting of motifs in pink, maroon, green and yellow with rosettes in green and pink; surrounded by a double border of flowers and triangles in purple, green, yellow and pink.

Cat. No. 19.

20 Carder's Bow (*Kaman-i-halaji*). Late 19th century.
Length 170 cms; sounding board 33×25 cms, Shiraz.
Shaft with five peg holes drilled along its length; waxed flax thread runs from top to bottom of the bow, to which is tied a bunch of twisted wool to cover the hand holding it.

The sounding board is drilled with nineteen peg holes and is attached to the shaft and reinforced with waxed cord. The outer edges of the board are lined with leather and the shaft end with a strip of rubber.

The end of the bow would be held above the pile of wool with the cord just touching the wool. When struck with a mallet, the vibrations from the cord separate the matted fibres and remove impurities from the wool.

21 Floor Felt (*Keçe*). *c.* 1960.
205×120 cms. Qashqā'i. Fars.
Single face, wool. FACE: Natural ground with field of three medallions, central one decorated with four peacocks; borders of triangles with six peacocks perched outside, in crimson, orange, green and blue.

Ordinarily used as floor covers in the tents but often have carpets laid on top of them.

22 Floor Felt (*Keçe*). *c.* 1960.
211·5×139 cms. Qashqā'i. Fars.
Single face, wool. FACE: Ivory field, pink, orange, green, blue and brown lozenge-medallions, and inner border of reciprocal triangles. Outer dark beige border.

23 Floor Felt (*Keçe*). *c.* 1960.
181×114 cms. Qashqā'i. Fars.
Single face, wool. FACE: Three lozenges in black each containing a small roundel on a grey field. Checked border, surrounded by brown.

Cat. No. 24.

24 Floor Felt (*Keçe*). 1970.
185×126 cms. Qashqā'i. Fars.
Single face, wool. FACE: A standing lion and stylized plants in purple, orange and green on a natural field, patterned borders and outer dark brown border. The design is taken from a group of pile carpets known as the "Lion Rugs of Fars". Dated 1970.

Cat. No. 23.

Cat. No. 25.

25 Floor Felt (*Keçe*). *c.* 1960.
172·5×113 cms. Qashqā'i. Fars.
Single face, wool. FACE: Natural buff field divided into three lozenges each containing a star in pink, orange, blue and black; triangular spaces filled with lozenges. Dark buff border.

26(b).

26 Felt Hat (*Bork*). 1970.
12 cms high, 21 cms long and 15·5 cms wide. Shiraz, Fars.
Natural beige felt hat, with high-domed crown, and two semi-circular flaps.

These can be pulled over the ears in cold weather or by changing the position of the hat, one flap acts as a brim to shade the eyes from the sun. This is a fairly recent introduction to Iran.

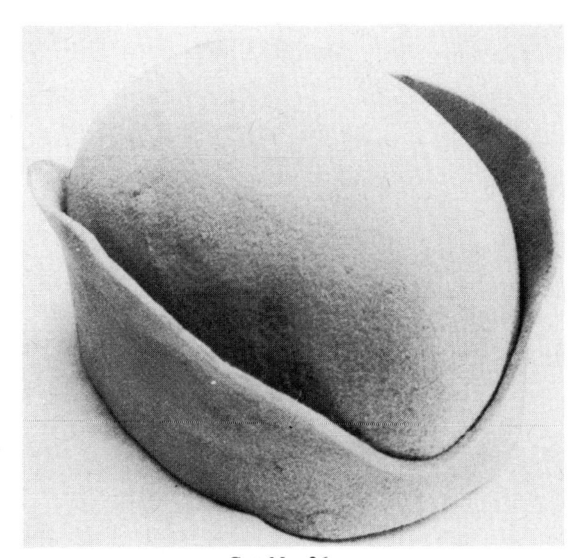

Cat. No. 26.

27 Shepherd's Cloak (*Kapanak*). *c.* 1970.
104×86 cms. Qashqā'i. Fars.
Heavy grey felt sleeved wool coat with round neck opening and open front.

28 Shepherd's Cloak (*Kapanak*). 1960.
103×70 cms. Sleeve flaps 61 cms. Qashqā'i. Fars.
Round neck with front opening decorated with rows of pink and brown stitching, narrow vestigial sleeves with closed rounded ends extend from shoulders to just above the lower hemline.

Made in one piece, of natural grey sheep and goat wool.

Cat. No. 27.

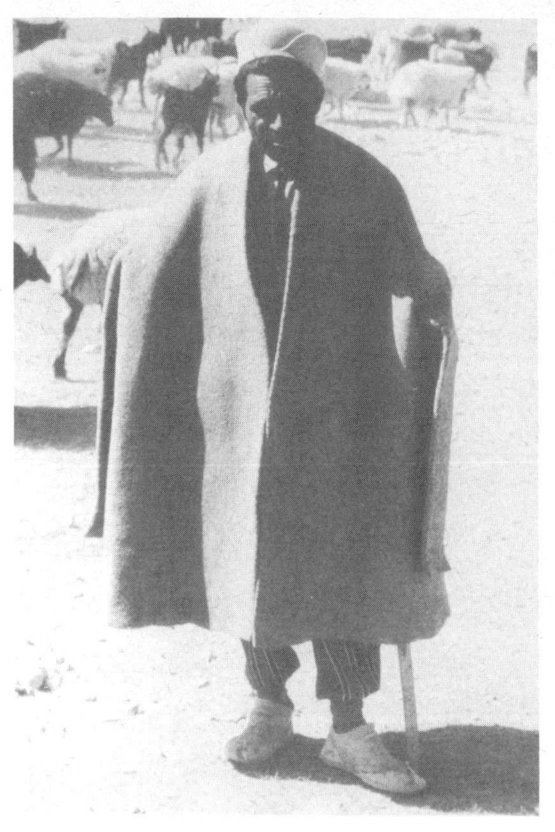

Cat. No. 28.

29 Saddle Felt (*Içirgi*). 1965.
79·5×99 cms. Qashqā'i. Fars.
Single face, wool. FACE: Natural grey, two layers felted together, semi-circular, the upper with cut zigzag edges superimposed, and a small purple and yellow plant spray in each corner.

Cat. No. 29.

Cat. No. 16.

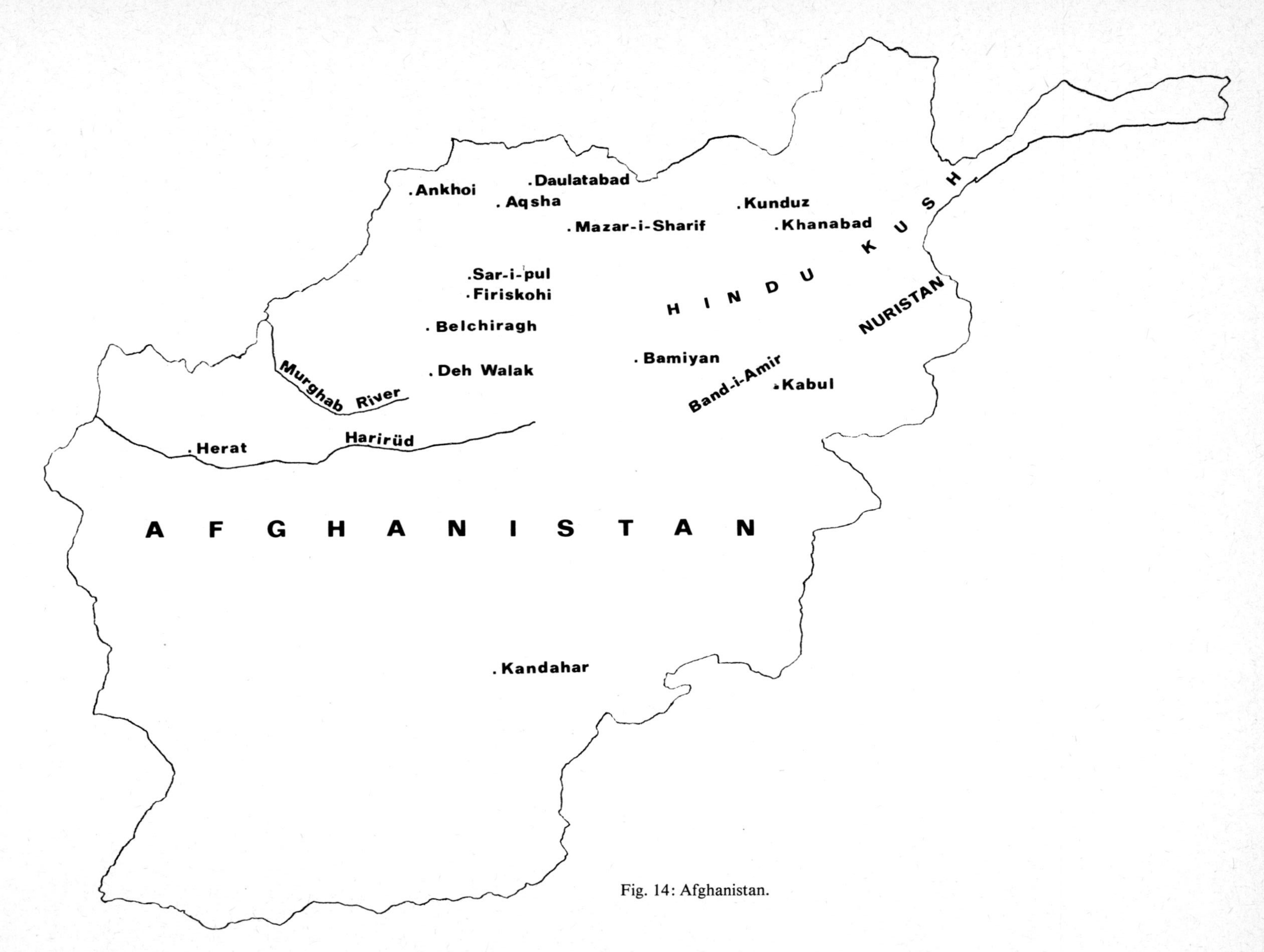

Fig. 14: Afghanistan.

AFGHANISTAN

During this century, thousands of Russian Uzbeks have come over to Afghanistan and brought their felt mats and wall-hangings with them. Although the original felts have perished, the designs have continued. There are Uzbek at Khanabad from Kunduz. I was told that it took one Uzbek woman one month to make an embroidered felt, and for a felt patchwork the same time.

The Lakai, a tough people who lived by their wits and raids on their neighbours, also left Russia in the 1920's and settled in Afghanistan north of the Hindu Kush. In the Eastern Bukharan Mountains they were known as the *Lakhé,* and continued being warrior-herdsmen (Lindahl and Knorr, 1975, p. 31). They still made felt and woven rugs, bags and many other artifacts with the patterns and symbols of their long artistic tradition (Lindahl and Knorr, 1975, p. 31). Today, they have borrowed some minor motifs from the Uzbek, Kirghiz and Kazakhs, which makes it difficult to be specific on all the symbols or origins. At the same time they have influenced the Uzbeks and encouraged them to embroider again as they used to do. The background of embroideries is often a very dark blue. The fact that they were no longer in their own environment not only lead to alien influences but caused a general degeneration in their own productions.

The Ersari Türkmen are the major felt makers and the main tribe of this group to be found still in Afghanistan (Pl. 51). Türkmen came to Afghanistan from Russia in this century and joined those Uzbeks, Baluchi and Lakai who were already there. Their work strongly resembles that made by Türkmen in Iran, or Southern Russia, and much felt is made even though some of the tribes are now settled. Despite the inevitable mingling of these people and mutual influence in method and type, some of the ethnic traditions and individual tribal designs and methods are identifiable.

The main centres of felt-making in Afghanistan are in the north and west, just south of the Russian border and north of Mazar-i-Sharif, where the most concentrated production of felt is to be found. Villages all over this area make it. At Boina Quara, 40 kilometres south west of Mazar, settled and nomad *kuchi* Uzbek do a great deal of embroidered felt (Cat. Nos. 38, 44). At Aqsha, 190 kilometres west of Mazar, and at Daulatabad north of Mazar, also at Bamiyan and Band-i Amir, felt is made. Kandahar is another felt-making centre in the south. To the west on the Iranian border near Herat, there are felts of a fairly simple nature. I was told recently that here, as in Turkey, when felts wear out they are recycled.

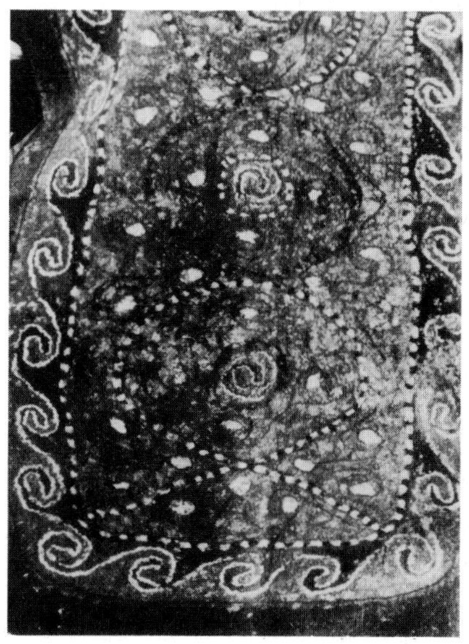

Pl. 51: Afghan rug with Türkmen pattern. N.E. Afghanistan. 1969.

Another felt-making area is the Kirghiz/Afghan frontier land, that long corridor in North-east Afghanistan bordered in the north by Russia, the south by Pakistan and the east by China. The nomads, no longer able to cross these frontiers, are much restricted in their wanderings. They still carry out their traditional felt-making. First, a group of five or six men and women beat the loose fleecy lumps of wool with a stick in each hand, standing in a semi-circle and alternating the strokes, five or six beats in a kind of phrase. When it is thoroughly loosened and dirt detached, they sprinkle boiling water on it and then subject it to pressure by rolling it back and forth in a straw mat as in North-east Iran. They also however, both men and women, use their forearms to roll it, while kneeling on the ground. Here in the north-east, in Nuristan, bordering Chitral and the Pakistan frontier, woven caps, felted on the outside, now replace the old felt ones. They are woven in two shades of brown and then felted to make them (a) warmer and (b) resemble the former type, (Cat. No. 55). Nuristan also produced felted ceremonial robes of goat hair and an example is in Kabul Museum. One is in the collection of Victoria, B.C., Canada.

Pl. 52a: Felt maker's tent at Deh Walak. Afghanistan. 1953.

Pl. 52b: *Yurts* at Belchiragh. Afghanistan. 1953.

Pl. 53a and b: Women laying felt for marriage felt. Belchiragh. Afghanistan. 1953.

Pl. 54: Men flinging rolled felt up and down at Belchiragh. Afghanistan. 1953.

H. W. Bellew described the *khozai,* a thick felt coat which took the place of the sheepskin coat *postin,* normally worn in the Peshawar frontier district. The *khozai,* peculiar to Kandahar and the country westwards, was made in shape rather similar to the *postin,* out of one large piece of felt with the sleeves sewn in later. The *khozai* weighed less than the *postin,* but was waterproof and very warm, and lasted a long time at least among the peasants as observed by Bellew (Bellew, 1862, p. 359).

Pl. 55a: A man supporting himself on tripod whilst kneading felt with his feet. Belchiragh. Afghanistan. 1953.

Pl. 55b: Man kneading felt with hands and feet. 1960.

In 1953 Lennart Edelberg, member of the Danish Scientific Mission to Afghanistan from the National Museum of Denmark, explored the little-visited area of Firiskohi south of Sar-i-Pul. There, north of the rivers Murghab and the Harirud, he visited two villages, Belchiragh and Deh Walak, where people could not recall a previous visit from Europeans. His series of pictures recorded the contemporary fabrication of felt in these two places (Pl. 52a, b). At Deh Walak a black tent was used in which to make the felt for a marriage. The felt covered the floor of the black tent, reserved for this purpose at the time. Inside the shelter of the tent two women worked, facing each other, on the coarse plain *kilim* used, in this case, as the ground on which to prepare the felt. First the edge of the mat was put down in piles of loose carded wool, then a ball of string was used to outline the pattern (Pl. 3a, b). One woman then made the pattern in clumps of white wool, working from left to right, while the second woman filled in the spaces with violet wool, working from right to left (Pl. 3b). Once having finished this and the wool all laid down, (Pl. 53a, b), the whole bundle was rolled up and the men took over the work. At Belchiragh, Lennart Edelberg photographed the men flinging the rolled felt up and down in preparation (Pl. 54) while one picture shows another man supporting himself on a tripod kneading the felt with his feet (Pl. 55a), while another elsewhere works with hands and feet (Pl. 55b).

The method in Afghanistan differs slightly from region to region. They lay the wool out on a cane mat, always laying the reverse side first, unlike in Iran where the upper pattern is usually put down first. The women make it. They sometimes pull it back and forth with a rope, where the men often help in the pushing and pulling over the matting (Pl. 46). Sometimes they put a big grey felt over it to protect it. They only use water and not soap as in Turkey. The methods of making up the felt articles used are numerous and include the following:

1. Strips of felt in decorative shapes sewn on to cotton bands.
2. Odd pieces of plain felt, sewn on to cotton bands.
3. Embroidered bits of felt on plain felt.
4. More complicated embroidered and stitched felts (Cat. No. 38).
5. Large pieces sewn on top.
6. Patchwork felt. (Cat. No. 42).
7. Relief borders, layer on layer. (Cat. No. 40).

The Türkmen here as elsewhere are the only people who decorate with designs properly felted on both sides, the reverse showing dots or lattice work.

The range of artifacts in felt is wide but to my knowledge includes the following:

1. Tent coverings for their *yurts* (Pl. 52a, b).
2. Felt socks with rubber over-shoes with pointed turned up toes.
3. Oblong rugs and mats; (Cat. No. 45, 42).
4. Round rugs, for the floors of the *yurts*, 3·5 and 4m across; these are made at Mazar and Aqsha by the settled and nomad people. (Pl. 17a, b).
5. Blankets and hangings for camels, donkeys, horses etc. (Cat. No. 39).
6. Bags for animals and for hanging in the *yurts*. (Cat. No. 47).
7. Long crockery bags (Lindahl and Knorr, 1975 p. 19) (Cat. No. 49a).
8. Square or shield-shaped wall hangings. (Cat. No. 48).
9. Hats (Lindahl and Knorr, 1975, p. 48).
10. Pachtoun coats for shepherds.
11. Horse trappings, e.g. saddle cloths. (Cat. No. 54).
12. Felt is sometimes used in a modern piece of jewellery, worn as a breastplate, where it shows through windows in the metal. (Cat. No. 56).

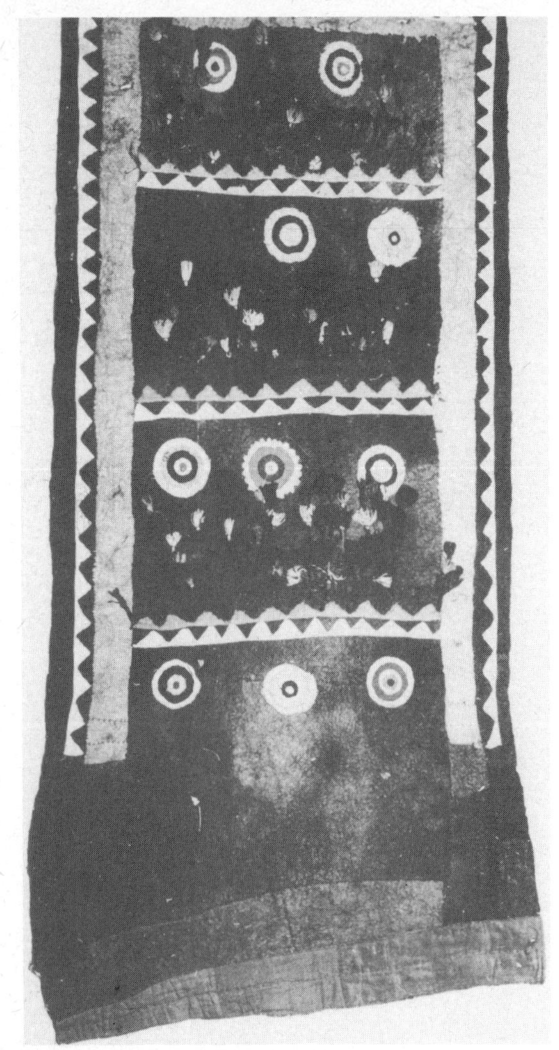

Cat. No. 36.

33 Floor Felt *c.* 1950.
244 x 169 cms. Hazara/Türkmen. C. Afghanistan.
Double face, wool. FACE: Rectangular field with rounded corners, containing 3 medallions, each with spiral motifs in orange, blue, crimson; guard stripes enclosing alternating dots; reciprocal saw-tooth pattern; "running hound" pattern; outer brown border. REVERSE: Patches of ivory, crimson, orange, blue on natural brown ground. Partial ragged coloured fringe.

34 Floor Felt *c.* 1960.
190×145 cms. N.W. Afghanistan.
Single face, wool. One of a pair of identical felts. FACE: Three lozenges containing maroon "horn" motif on an ochre background. Patterns outlined in black; border with reciprocal volutes and outer grey border.

35 Floor Felt *c.* 1960.
145×110 cms. N.W. Afghanistan.
Single face, wool. FACE: Three lozenges each containing maroon "horn" motif on natural ivory ground, surrounded by reciprocal volutes and black outer border.

36 Wall Hanging *c.* 1950.
206×94 cms. Nuristan.
Double face, wool. FACE: Maroon field with strips of cloth stitched on, notched and tasselled; roundels, roughly cut and stitched on, of concentric circles of cloth; border of orange; outer border of brown; at the top patches of felt and cloth stitched together. REVERSE: Field of orange and maroon; outer border of brown and at the top patches of natural ivory.

37 Felt Prayer Mat 1950.
110·5×67 cms. Nuristan.
Single face, wool. FACE: Field of light and dark brown, divided into three panels by lines of red and white chain stitch and forming prayer niche, flanked on either side by two borders embroidered in white, and red and white chain stitch enclosing scrolls. Fringed edges.

38 Large Floor Felt 1976.
195×103 cms. Kunduz.
Single face, wool. FACE: Four rows of "Trees of Life" on a black ground (cf. Iranian felt No. 5) in white, maroon, purple, red, blue, yellow and green, separated by lines of cross stitch, embroidered multi-coloured border edged with cord. Fringed at ends. (Col. Pl. 6). Made by Golbubu women.

39 Horse Cloth *c.* 1920.
163×113 cms. Kunduz.
Woven coarse cloth cover, lined with thick natural mixed felt. Wider at the front to protect shoulders. Quilted through both layers with orange, brown, purple and grey stitches forming a variety of scroll and horn patterns. Edged with woven braid, and fringed with brown tassels.

40 Floor Felt *c.* 1950.
190×97 cms. Ankhoi.
Single face, wool. FACE: Natural ivory ground. Field: geometric designs in black, orange and buff on purple; enclosed by a buff coloured appliqué border of dog tooth pattern of alternating orange and purple triangles surrounded by an appliqué border of purple and orange. Natural buff outer border fringed with purple and orange.

Cat. No. 39.

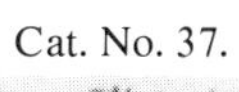

Cat. No. 37.

Cat. No. 40.

41 Felt Rug 1970.
194×126 cms. Mazar-i-Sharif.
Single face, wool. FACE: Field of loosely formed triangles and lozenges in red, white, yellow and brown, each with a centre spot in black, bordered on three sides by orange and red lines: surrounded by a pattern of volutes "running hound" in black and red edged in orange. Field enclosed within reciprocal patterns in black and white, with guard stripes in purple and yellow. Outer brown/black border.

42 Large Felt 1976.
342 × 140 cms. Shulgara aq Kobruk. Near Boina Qara (60 kms south west of Mazar-i-Sharif).
Single face of patchwork, wool. FACE: Field of four squares enclosing "horn" motifs in alternating colours of red and blue enclosed by a border of alternating brown and ivory triangles; reciprocal patterned borders in red, orange, dark brown and ivory.

43 Floor Felt *c.* 1930.
191×97 cms. Uzbek.
Single face, wool. FACE: Natural ivory field containing three lozenges defined by embroidered border in dark brown woollen cord, each enclosing scroll designs in pink and green; surrounded by a border of interlocking triangles containing scrolls and linear motifs in red and brown.

44 Floor Felt *c.* 1970.
266×119 cms. Uzbek/Lakai.
Single face, wool. FACE: Field of three lozenges each containing four patterned panels in blue, green, white and yellow on red; surrounded by triangular patterns of scrolls in yellow, red and green. Field enclosed by a border of alternating blue-green motifs. Black border in chain stitch with a tassel at each corner. (Col. Pl. 7).

Cat. No. 41.

Cat. No. 42.

Cat. No. 43.

Cat. No. 45.

Cat. No. 46 Reverse.

Cat. No. 46.

◄ Cat. No. 47.

Cat. No. 50.

45 Felt Rug *c.* 1970.
204×103 cms. Uzbek/Lakai.
Single face, wool. FACE: Field of three lozenges with symmetrical patterns in purple, green, yellow, white and dark blue chain – and red coral-knot stitching; lozenges contained within panelled border of Roman/filling stitch; remaining triangles infilled with similarly stitched motifs. Orange panelled border, each panel containing a "horn" motif in blue and green coral-knot stitch. Outer black border edged in raised chain-stitch and fringed at the ends with white cord.

46 Felt Rug 1970.
157×84 cms. Uzbek/Lakai.
Double face, wool. FACE: Field of three lozenges containing motifs in green, purple, blue and red on black in coral-knot and chain stitch edged in red and green cross stitch; surrounded by beige triangles containing "horn" patterns; border of "horn" motifs. Outer black border edged in raised chain stitch in red and blue. The rug is fringed at both ends with turquoise, red, white, purple and blue cords. REVERSE: Three lozenges on white rectangular field with two plain borders.

47 Felt Cushion Face 1960.
54×50 cms. Uzbek/Lakai.
Single face, wool. FACE: Central medallion with four interlocking rams' horns, *sekiz ghocak,* in white and yellow coral-knot stitch. Outer border with embroidered rams' horns in coral-knot stitch; fringed in yellow, purple, grey, pink and orange tasselled cords. The back is lined with printed cotton.

48 Felt Bag Face/Shield 1970
56·5×56·5 cms. Uzbek/Lakai.
Single face, wool. FACE: Central medallion containing symmetrical pattern in coral-knot and chain stitch in blue, red and orange on black; surrounded by a border of panels in green, white, blue and orange on orange, in Roman/filling stitch edged in detached-chain and coral-knot stitch. Outer black border edged in raised chain stitch and braided and fringed along one side with green cord.

◄ Cat. No. 48.

Cat. No. 49(a).

Cat. No. 49(b).

49 Tent Bag/Strut Pouch 1970
69 × 37 cms. Mazar-i-Sharif.
Two-sided bag. Side (a): red ground with hooked patterns in dark brown fish bone and button hole stitching, edged in white chain stitch; star motifs.

Top bordered with panels in couching and green button hole filling stitch. Bottom, decorated with hooked pattern enclosing star in couching.

Side (b): panels of couching and button hole stitching alternating with hooked patterns in dark brown, edged with chain stitch; leading to a pattern of brown triangles in button hole stitch edged in white chain stitch. Five bunches of horsehair tied with strips of cotton hang from lower edges.

50 Tent Bag/Strut Pouch 1965.
61×32 cms. Uzbek/Lakai. Mazar-i-Sharif.
Two-sided bag. Side (a): Red ground. A curvilinear swastika is enclosed within a lozenge of dark brown fish bone stitch, edged in white chain stitch from which branch four pairs of "horns". Above and below this are hooked patterns in the same stitching; top of the bag edged in raised chain stitch and oversewn in brown and cream on three sides; lower edges decorated with plaits holding bunches of horsehair. The bag is quilted inside with multi-coloured cottons. Side (b) is similar.

Cat. No. 51.

Cat. No. 52.

51 Donkey's Felt Rump Band 1970.
109×52·5 cms. Uzbek/Lakai.
Panels of red felt edged with blue and yellow stitches embroidered with dark brown motifs and edged in white chain stitch. Top band decorated with six bunches of horse hair, flanks heavily tasselled with tufts of horse hair on plaited wool. The whole piece is lined with plain and patterned cottons; front edges of the rump band are adorned with orange and blue woollen tassels.

52 Donkey's Felt Rump Band 1970.
91×42 cms. Uzbek/Lakai.
Panels of red felt edged with dark blue and yellow stitches, embroidered with dark brown motifs, edged with white chain stitch. The top band is decorated with three bunches of dyed horse hair; flanks heavily tasselled with plaited wool wrapped with coloured cotton strips each terminating in a tuft of horse hair.

Cat. No. 53.

53 Donkey Breast Band 1960.
134×10 cms. Northern Afghanistan.
Felt ground with flat stitch in brown, red and yellow with a triangular felt amulet covered in cotton and with tassels in blue, red, orange and brown along the lower edge.

54(a) Horse Blanket or Tent decoration *c.* 1970.
251×98 cms. Tekke Türkmen.
Natural ivory ground with lattice pattern of woollen cord and tassels in red and blue on borders and extending in lines across the blanket.

(b) Horse Blanket or Tent decoration *c.* 1920.
284×117 cms. Türkmen.
Natural ivory ground with lattice pattern of felted woollen cord and tassels in red, blue and yellow-green on borders, extending in lines across the blanket. Central panel of red and yellow motifs; stitched border of felted woollen cord containing horn motifs in red, yellow-green and blue.

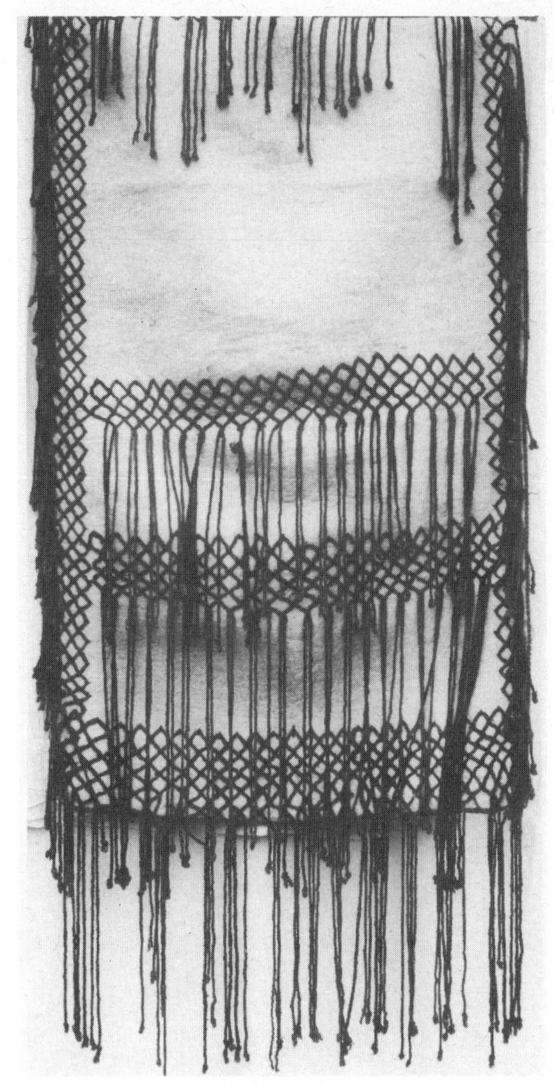

Cat. No. 54(a).

See Cat. No. 55.

55 (a) Woven Hat *Chitrali Patti Cap.* 1978.
20 cms diam. Bought in Peshawar.
Natural brown woollen cap, woven on a handloom, seamed by machine, and felted on outside to give protection.

(b) Woven Hat 1978.
20 cms diam. Jellalabad.
Light brown woollen cap woven on handloom, felted on outside to give more protection.

56 Breast Plate 19th/20th century
23 × 22.5 cms Türkmen. Mazar-i-Sharif.
Brass; inlays of silver, filigree work, 36 cabochon cornelians, red and green felt insets in lower half. The central cylinder is hollow, opening at each end to contain prayers etc. 22 bells hang by chains, held by string. The plate is hung from an embroidered band, decorated in silver thread.

Cat. No. 56.

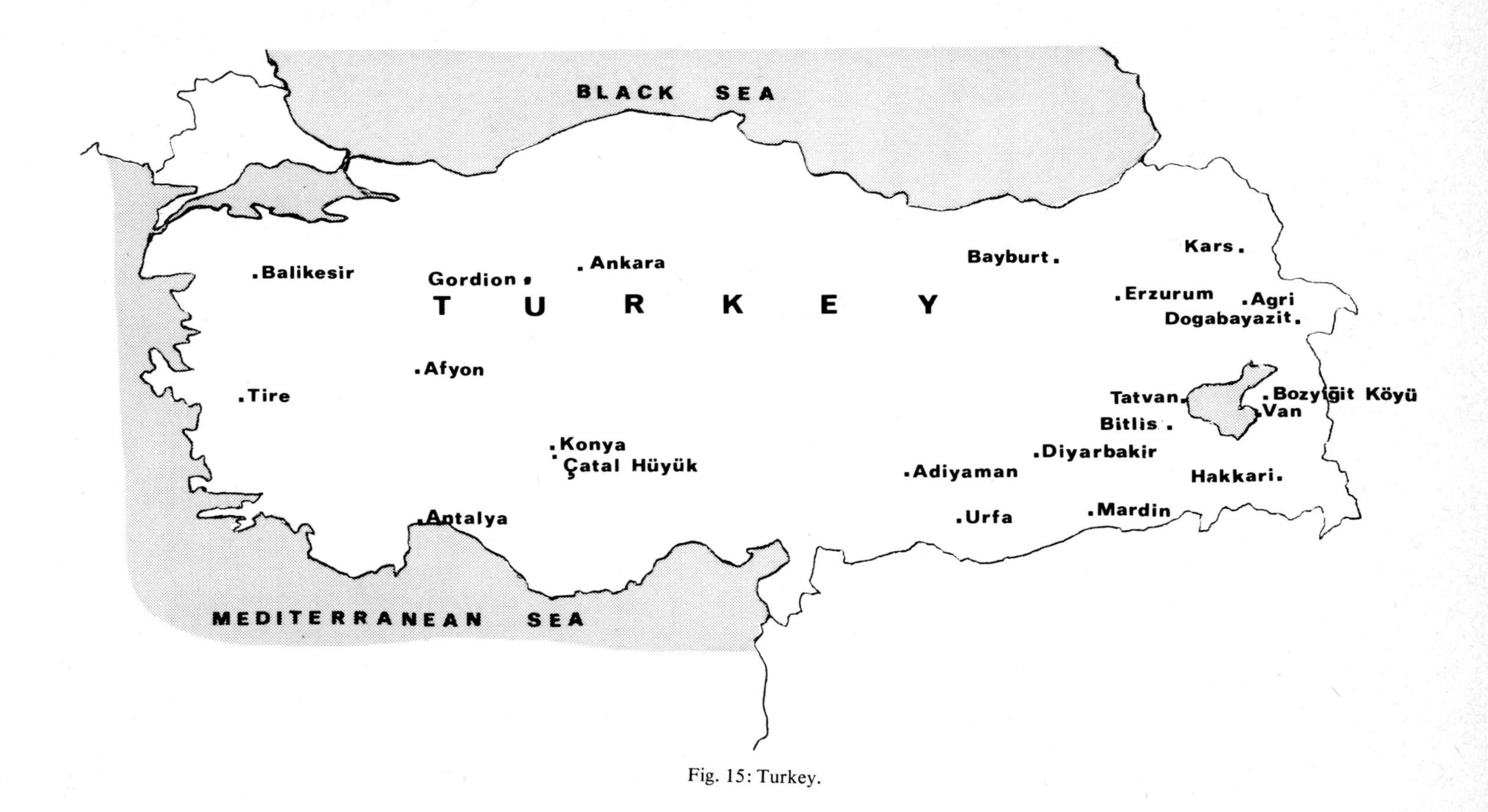

Fig. 15: Turkey.

TURKEY

In Eastern Turkey felt* is disappearing with alarming rapidity. Where once there was felt now there is synthetic imported material or plastic. Although it is still possible to see the thick brown undecorated felt under donkey saddles from Dogabayazit, Kars, Agri, Van, Tatvan and from Bitlis to Diyarbakir, felt mats are rarely to be seen. Very rarely the remains of an old brown and white or red and yellow spotted felt may be seen cut up for padding saddles or repairing straps, *aşirmas,* in saddlers' shops (Cat. No. 76b). Adiyaman has a flourishing saddler's industry where the re-use of old felts can be found both for making the underside of saddles and lining the wooden collars.

The one artifact which is still seen everywhere is the shepherd's felt cloak, *kepenek* (Pl. 22, 36; Col. Pl. 5b). These are natural, ivory, grey, or brown, made from sheep's wool, or a combination of sheep's wool and goat hair, and essential in the cold penetrating winds. A shepherd now often finds a large plastic bag and slitting it down one side envelops himself and his *kepenek* in it! The brown *kepeneks* are made in all parts of Turkey, while the ivory and grey ones are made in centres such as Hakkari, Mardin, Urfa and Bayburt, besides the main western distribution centres of Konya and Afyon, Balikesir and Tire (Landreau, 1978, p. 14 map) (Cat. Nos. 65, 66, 67a, b).

When travelling in Eastern Turkey in 1962, I saw many patterned felt mats. Recent visits revealed none. A number of very interesting animal trappings are still however used in the south east around Van and Hakkari. These include camel headdresses, made of felt and often decorated with beads, embroidery and shells (Cat. Nos. 73 and 74). There are felt-based charms for hanging inside tents to keep off the evil eye (Cat. No. 70). Both trappings and charms have been carefully kept for many years because of the magical properties attributed to them.

Since 1970, Veronika Gervers has been studying felt-making in Anatolia, at Konya, Balikesir, Tire, and Afyon (Landreau, 1978, p. 14). She, too, has found this ancient craft rapidly being superseded by modern products and she has dealt in depth with method and production in Turkey (M. & V. Gervers, 1974, pp. 15-28). Her researches have shown that various local differences occur, for example, in the "stepping" process (treading on the felt to harden it) (M. & V. Gervers, 1974, pp. 15-28) which is not always done twice, and unrolling for inspection and re-rolling, which seldom occurs in Iran. During the stepping process,

* In Turkish, *keçe* the same form as used by Türkmen in Iran.

Fig. 16: Felt stepping, adding pressure by placing hands on knees.

extra pressure is sometimes applied by pressing the hands hard on the knees (Fig. 16). The fulling in Turkey, which is the next process of shrinking the felt, is carried out by beating it with a mallet when wet. Even now, the felt is occasionally hardened by attaching it to a horse, and having it dragged along the ground. This old custom was often mentioned in relation to felting by the Mongols. It is during the fulling that any re-shaping and joining of hoods or capes is done.

There used to be many felt guilds in Turkey and a few still exist today. This method of manufacture is quite different from that in Iran, where felt is usually made by families. The family emblem of the master of the guild is often found stamped in blue or red on Turkish felt coats (Cat. No. 65), but in recent years these Turkish felt makers who are often itinerant, are less in demand. The carding machine, adopted rapidly over the last fifteen years in the flourishing felt-making centres of Western Turkey, has supplanted the bow and mallet in many places. Its speed allows a felt-maker to make seven or eight coats a day instead of two when using bow and mallet. Hardening can also be carried out by machine, replacing manual fulling and the traditional stepping process for hardening. It is interesting that it is the excellent railway service which has at least helped the felting of coats to survive. The industry as a whole is dying and with the methods used for centuries the traditional designs and customs are dying too. Modern heeled shoes wear out felt carpets more quickly, and ten years is about as long as a felt can survive, whereas in earlier years a felt carpet might have lasted for fifty years. A shepherd's coat probably has a life of about three years, but perhaps four or five years in a poor family.

Pl. 56: Typical cartwheel and geometric designs, Konya. 1958.

Several regions have been suggested as the source of the carding bow; some believe that it came from Western Europe in the Middle Ages, being used for cotton, others believe it was introduced from China. Further east it is not used, so this and the use of the fork for turning the felt seem to be innovations in Western Turkey (cf. Chap. 1, p. 2).

In 1975 Miss Rosalind Wade kindly visited some felt-making centres for me and found the tall felt hats of the whirling Dervishes still made at Konya (Cat. No. 58). Only one master continues to make these and only the Dervishes are allowed to wear them. Another felt-maker still making rugs told her that he had no prototypes for the patterns, but remembered clearly all the traditional patterns. His family had been in business for 200-300 years, and believed that the tradition of felt-making in Anatolia came from the Hittites. He used chemical dyes and to make a rug he set out the patterns on a large rush mat. The patterns were formed by putting the coloured pieces of thin felt in geometrical and cartwheel type designs (Pl. 56; Cat. No. 72). He worked very quickly and deftly, cutting strips, diamonds and sawlike edges and placing them out spontaneously. Great attention was paid to symmetry and lengthwise machine lines binding the matting underneath gave a guide line. Although the felt used to make the pattern was thin and loosely made and fragile, the actual carpets when made were *c.* 1-2 cms thick. When the pattern was completed, loose white wool (apparently lamb's wool because the strands must be short) was tossed on top of the three central cartwheels with a kind of wooden rake. About six layers of wool were laid and each covered with water, and then rolled up in the matting and put into a simple press (for about ten hours) which rotated with a hammer weighing about 45 kgs. The shop where all this went on was tiny – *c.* 3 by 8 m and had a storage loft above covering about two-thirds of the shop. Twenty years ago, before they had a mechanised press, the men had pressed the matting with their feet. A random selection of two felt-making shops in Afyon in 1978 showed that the makers' sons were carrying on the craft, and that felts were being sold over a wide area of East Turkey.*

It might be of interest to note that in two Syrian felt centres, Aleppo and Hama, Rosalind Wade found the method of felt-making much the same as that in Turkey, though in Aleppo the felts were not as thick as those in Turkey. In Hama she found at least twenty felt-makers' shops, 6 m by 3 m, stone vaulted with little lofts for storage. They also had adopted the carding machine by 1975. Designs on their felts included flowers and stylized birds. Damascus used to be an active centre for hand-made felt but recently there too machines have been introduced.

In 1978 I spent some more time in Eastern Turkey and in the village of Bozyiğit Köyü, some 20 miles N.E. of Van. The headman received us and I was able to photograph felt coats, *kepeneks,* being worn by young shepherds (Col. Pl. 4b). They said their felt coats came from Urfa and Mardin but that the brown felt was made in the village. No rugs were to be seen, and like most settled Turks they could not understand anyone being so interested in felt. Throughout Eastern Turkey there was a similar situation.

* This information was supplied by W. Alp, who kindly purchased some of the Turkish felts in the exhibition.

57 Felt Fragments (*c.* 3000-2700 B.C.).
Beycesultan.
Fragments from thick patches of felt found by Seton Lloyd and James Mellaart at Beycesultan *c.* 1958.
Seton Lloyd and Mellaart, 1962, Vol. 1, p. 45.

Cat. No. 58.

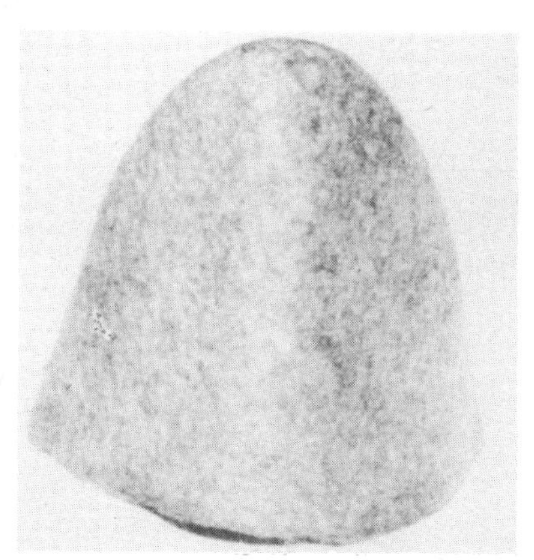

Cat. No. 59.

58 Felt Hat (*Sikke*). 1976.
26 (ht.) × 19·5 (diam.) cms. Konya.
Natural brown wool. Stiffened, possibly from being made on a wooden block. The hat maker was the late Ali Sapmaz of Konya, who at his death was said to be the last Dervish felt hat maker. These hats were made for the Mevlevi Dervishes.

59 Felt Hat (*Takke*). 1976.
19 (ht.) × 20 (diam.) cms. Ödemiş.
Light brown natural wool. Would be worn by Dervishes on less formal occasions.

60 Felt Hat (*Fes*). 1977.
12 (ht.) × 19 (diam.) cms. Konya.
Dark maroon wool with black tassel; stiffened interior with a pink lining. Made by Ali Sapmaz.

Cat. No. 60.

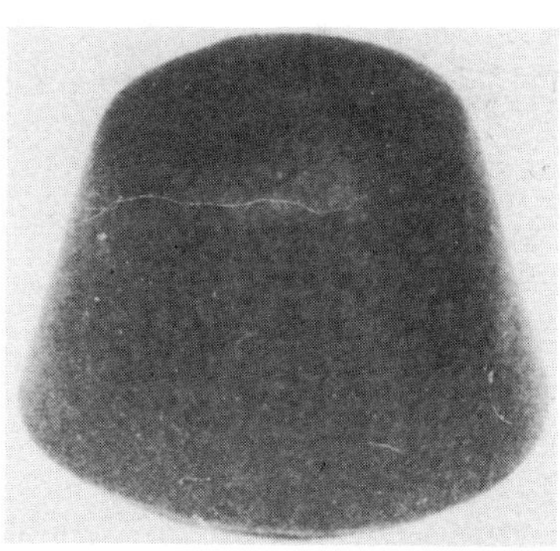

Cat. No. 61.

61 Felt Hat (*Fes*). 1976.
12 (ht.) × 18 (diam.) cms. Konya.
Maroon wool. The stiffened top indicates that it is not hand made.

Cat. No. 65.

62 Felt Hat (*Şapka*). 1978.
00 (ht.) x 00 (diam.) cms. Afyon.
Bought from the shop of Kemal Erkuş.

63 Felt Hat (*Şapka*). 1978.
00 (ht.) x 00 (diam.) cms. Afyon.
Bought from the shop of Kemal Erkuş.

64 Felt Hat (*Fes*). 1978.
12 (ht.) x 19 (diam.) cms. Istanbul.
Red felt hat with black tassel. Felt hats were worn until Ataturk forbade their use, and peaked caps came into fashion. The fez (fes) is now made for the tourist market by mechanical means.

65 Shepherd's Felt Cloak (*Kepenek*). 1978.
148×84 cms. Bayburt.
Natural ivory hooded cloak with central opening. Two red stars on either side are surrounded by blue triangles. The words AD OĞLU denote the son of the owner of the family business Haci Karabey Davutoğullari, felt and sack shop, Erzurum, who distribute them.

66 Shepherd's Felt Cloak (*Kepenek*). 1978.
143×80 cms. Van.
Natural brown hooded cloak with central opening. The initials F.H.6 in orange on the front denote the maker's name. Two star-like motifs in red and orange decorate the front.

67 (a) Shepherd's Felt Cloak (*Kepenek*). 1978.
145×85 cms. Afyon.
Cloak with decorated hood. Made from local wool in November 1978 by Şerafettin Arpaözü and his two sons. This workshop only deals in *kepeneks* and makes 30-40 per week.

(b) Shepherd's Felt Cloak (*Kepenek*). 1977.
161·5×93 cms. Söke (but probably made in Afyon).
Natural ivory hooded cloak with central opening, with red and blue star and other motifs decorating the front. The felt of this cloak is exceptionally thick, reaching 1·5 cms in places.

68 Felt Soles (*Taban*). 1978.
29×9·2 cms. Van.
Felt soles mainly in coarse brown goat hair. Worn by men inside boots or shoes to prevent sweat and provide ventilation. Brand name Temel. Size 44.

Cat. No. 69.

69 Felt Bag (*Heybe*). 1978.
46×36 cms. Bayburt.
Natural white felt with plaited cord shoulder strap. Decorated on the one side with artificial leather appliqué motifs edged with red velvet and four tassels. Bag sold in Erzurum at Haci Karabey Davutoğullari.

70 Charm (*Tilsim*). 1st quarter 20th century.
37 (diam.) cms. Kurdish; Cilo mountains.
Circular wall hanging on a felt base covered with ikatted cotton; decorated with a central mirror and radiating lines of cowrie shells *Şeytan Kabuğu* – the eight spaces filled with buttons, coins and felt cut out flowers, surrounded by a double border of shells enclosing buttons. The lower half of the charm is fringed with yellow silk cords, behind which are tufts of red, green and purple wool. Attached to the back are five plaited bands each separated into three bunches whipped with red, green, purple, orange and black wool and ending in a tassel of the same. The bands are joined together with four brass buttons.

Cat. No. 70. ►

71 Felt Rug (*Keçe*). 1978.
00 × 00 cms. Afyon.
Made in November 1978 at the workshop of Kemal Erkuş.

72 Felt Rug (*Keçe*) fragment. 1958.
140×97·5 cms. Konya.
Single face, wool. FACE: Greenish-grey ground covered with natural brown, the remains of circles (cartwheels) in blue, red and lime green. The rest of the field infilled in white and flanked by linear motifs, enclosed by a border of lozenges in blue and white. REVERSE: brown. Very worn example but showing the way the different layers are superimposed.

Cat. No. 72.

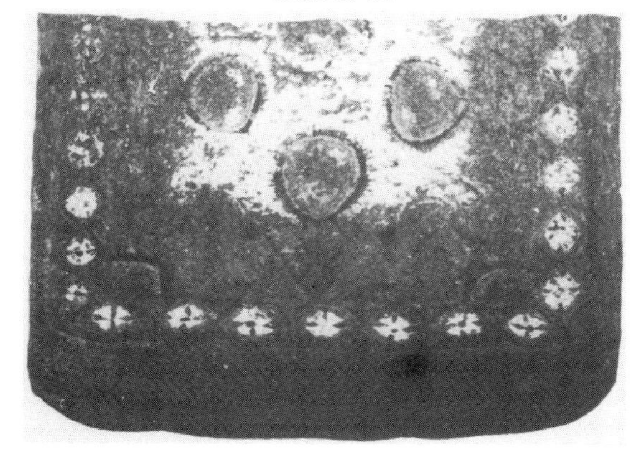

73 Camel Headdress (*Deve Başliği*). 1813/1814.
40×50 cms. Cerkan; Cilo Mountains.
From a circular piece of felt with coloured tassels covering the crown of the head, are suspended eight bands richly decorated with shells; from which hangs a circular band and two side flaps heavily encrusted with beads. Two metal rings attached with coarse stitches separate the side flaps from the nine tassels on the nose and the projecting clump of horse hair. The headdress is dated 1229 (after Hijra) and carries the inscription Allah – God. Below the date is a yellow beaded lion probably originally in combat with a horned animal.

74 Camel Headdress (*Deve Başliği*). *c.* 1940.
39×50 cms Kurdish; Cilo Mountains.
Blue and red felt head covering consisting of side, neck and nose flaps decorated with a variety of white buttons with cowries, "devil shells", *Şeytan Kabuğu,* round the borders of the ear-flaps. There are 14 mirrors, with star-like metal surrounds and the two bands of felt joining the flaps going over the top of the head are surmounted with orange and natural wool tassels with a smaller orange tassel on the nose flap. A chin strap is attached to two iron rings. These were used until fairly recently. They are now retained for weddings and festive occasions.

Cat. No. 73.

Cat. No. 74.

75 Felt Band (*Keçe*). 1978.
107×10·5×1·5 cms. Adiyaman.
Padding to a leather strap for donkey or horse.

76 (a) Breech Strap (*Aşirma*). 1977.
84×13 cms. Trabzon.
Padded felt band. Underside of brown felt, decorated on top with a strip of red, brown, ochre, green and blue *kilim*, sewn together by long rows of chain stitch and edged with purple and white plaited cotton. The strap would have been fastened to the rest of the donkey harness by means of the two attached loops.

(b) Breech Strap (*Aşirma*). 1978.
69·5×8·5 cms. Adiyaman.
Off-cut of felt, in brown, yellow and red on a natural ground backed by a double layer of canvas webbing using running stitches in black. Attached to one end is an iron ring. The opposite end has canvas left loosely protruding to enclose a strap.

Cat. No. 76(a) (left).

Cat. No. 76(b) (far left).

It is perhaps not surprising that the tradition of felt-making has survived in Russia to this day, as it is there, in the Pazyryk Collection, that the richest earliest extant examples of the craft can be seen (Col. Pl. 1; Pl. 12). It is made in many districts and known as *koshma* or *voilok.* Moreover, felt artifacts have been collected by the Museum of Oriental Art in Moscow, where there are over fifty felts (Beresneva, 1976).

On account of the vast size of Russia and the distribution of the various ethnic groups, styles varying according to method and design have emerged. For example, the Türkmen in the areas of Samarkand, Tashkent and Bukhara, still use *yurts,* although today the inhabitants are referred to, in Russia, as shepherds rather than nomads. Their felts are rather similar to other Türkmen examples in Iran or Turkey. The Yomut Türkmen in particular persist in making types of rug long since abandoned by other tribes, for example the five-sided decorative flank hangings for camels (Fig. 18).

Fig. 18: Reconstructed five-sided flank hanging for a camel.

The Kazakhs and Kirghiz make heavily embroidered quilted felts, usually in yellow and red on black, brown or white backgrounds and with oversewn edges to the motifs (Col. Pl. 8). Work by makers such as Stybaeva Katsha has been bought by the Oriental Museum, Moscow, as recently as 1960. The felts by Kazakhs and Kirghiz are similar in style and take a long time to make up after the actual felting has been done. They are made very well in the Alma Ata district of Kirghizstan. Some are made as floor covers such as those made by the Türkmen, e.g. their small rug from Suhana bought in 1970; Kirghiz, Kazakh and Georgian felts, however, are also made as bedcovers, wall-hangings and decorative objects. Cord is often introduced in the quilting, being oversewn on to the felt, while the motifs themselves are sometimes edged with braid and herring-bone stitch. The overall effect of those methods produces the firm finish which gives a Kirghiz felt a much longer life than a plain felted Türkmen example.

The tradition of stitched felts in Russia is well documented in many of the descriptions left by Sir Aurel Stein (Stein, 1928, Vol. I., p. 70) as well as in the examples in the Pazyryk Collection (Rudenko, 1970). Saddles shown in the Exhibition *From the Lands of the Scythians* (Metropolitan Museum, 1976, Cat. No. 112) showed rampant animals outlined with cord and in appliqué work.

Georgia does not make pile rugs, as not being Moslems there is not that very strong tradition of making them, but they make felts on an even earlier tradition. In West Georgia, a very fine and specific tradition has been preserved in quilted felts of good quality made in the villages by women. The quality is judged by weight, the thicker and firmer they are, the better. It is interesting to see how many of the early methods, such as mosaic work, "antique seam" for joining them as well as straight quilting, already used in the Pazyryk examples, have recently been practised. It is probably impossible to ascribe these techniques today entirely, and with certainty, to tradition as the techniques could have been derived more recently from the examples in the Hermitage. The word for felt in Georgia *nabadi* is very similar to the word *namad* used further south down the Caspian coast in Iran. Most famous contemporary felts from Georgia are made in Joushetia. One of the best known makers, whose work of 1950 is in the Moscow Collection, is Mehedleshoili Maria from Zemo-Alvani, a village in the Ahmet district (Fig. 19).

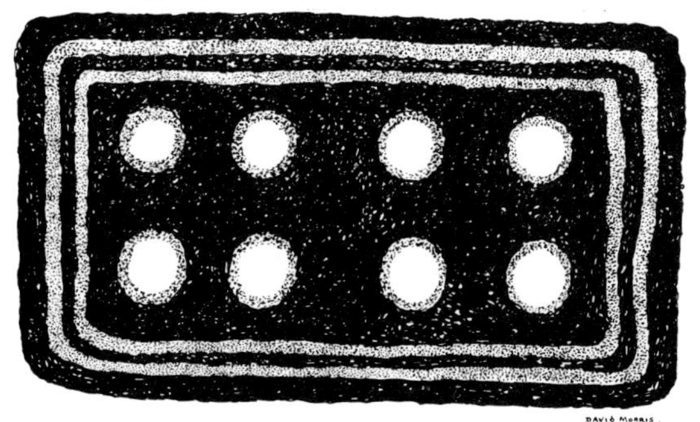

Fig. 19: Felt from Georgia by Mehedleshoili Maria. 174×96 cms. 1950.

BARENTS SEA
KOLA
Archangelsk
BALTIC SEA
Leningrad
Moscow
U. S. S. R.
Semipalatinsk
Altai Mountains
KAZAKHSTAN
Alma Ata
KIRGHIZSTAN
ARAL SEA
Tashkent
UZBEKISTAN
Khokand
TÜRKMEN
Khiva
Bukhara
Samarkand
Turkestan
YOMUT
TEKKE
ERSARI
SALOR
SARYK
BLACK SEA
CAUCASUS
GEORGIA
ARMENIA
CASPIAN SEA

Fig. 17: U.S.S.R.

Apart from rugs and wall-hangings and covers, the heavy long cape (*burka*) was still used as late as 1942 in Russia (Ch. 6). Ella Maillart found it in the Russian valley south of the Caucasus near Svanetia – "white felt hats, conical in shape, are worn by the men in these Svanetian villages" – she noted the felt-walled *yurts* and wrote, "Four women go through the first process of making felt. With wands that whistle through the air they beat on camel wool, which will later be wetted and rolled into a thick quilt". She also noted felt boots and described the making of the *yurts*: "over this umbrella-shaped frame they lay big squares of felt held down by broad plaited straps" (Maillart, 1942).

Today, after the felt has first been rolled, it is left in the unfinished state for better compactness, and later the rolling is resumed (Beresneva, 1976, p. 6) (cf. Chap. 1. p. 3 for a completely opposing view). It is done by women from different families. The Mongolian nomads do not use the reed mat on which to roll the felt, but use an old felt, calling it "mother of felt" or "daughter of felt" (M. & V. Gervers, 1974, p. 28).

One other group of felts remains. It is of interest not so much for its felt which soon became factory-made in the 19th century, but for its embroidery and social significance. This is the embroidered cloth made in Samarkand as late as the 18th-19th centuries, probably as girls' dowries. A superb 18th century example is illustrated in *Textile Collections of the World* (Lubell, 1976, Vol. 1, p. 122). The work is done with a silk thread in chain or couched (Bukhara) stitch, through two layers of cloth – one silk, the other linen. The whole area is covered with a most intricate embroidery. They became popular export items in the 19th and 20th centuries and many were made in Samarkand for the Indian market, and were bought in such places as Kashmir. A very fine 19th century example of the latter belongs to Abbot Hall. (Cat. No. 77).

This is of course not a complete survey of the U.S.S.R. and its felt, but just a few examples.

77 Tablecloth Mid 19th century.
230×180·5 cms. Samarkand.
Felted cloth field containing roundels of naturalistic and more stylized patterns in appliqué work and chain stitch; guard stripe of yellow felted cloth and an outer blue border with red flowers and linked tendrils.

This type of work was made as part of a dowry; also as an export material for the Indian market, particularly Kashmir.

78 Folding Screen Early 19th century.
165×60 cms. Mongolia.
Folding screen with three felted cloth embroidered and patchwork panels, each depicting a window with an arched top; in each window-niche stands a vase with flowers and foliage in three shades of red, blue, green, yellow, brown and black. Houses with dark windows, doorways and red roofs, with tall trees, can be seen in the background.

The composition is reminiscent of Tibetan *tankas* where a central panel is surrounded by a border made up of several unrelated pieces of fabric, or is possibly imitating earlier patchwork felt. This can be regarded as a piece of Mongolian Chinoiserie with Turkish elements. The Chinese influence is obvious in the Sinocized flowers but the embroideress has not understood the tripods which are placed on their sides in the top and lower borders.

79 Collar and Cuffs *c*. 1920.
Collar length 113 cms, cuff 26 cms. Mongolia.
Felt appliqué on felt outlined by a cloud pattern. Decorated with trefoils and "fish scales" in chain stitch, machine embroidery and piping.

Cf. Felt *Shabrack* in Mound 5 at Pazyryk, (Rudenko, 1970, Pl. 161).

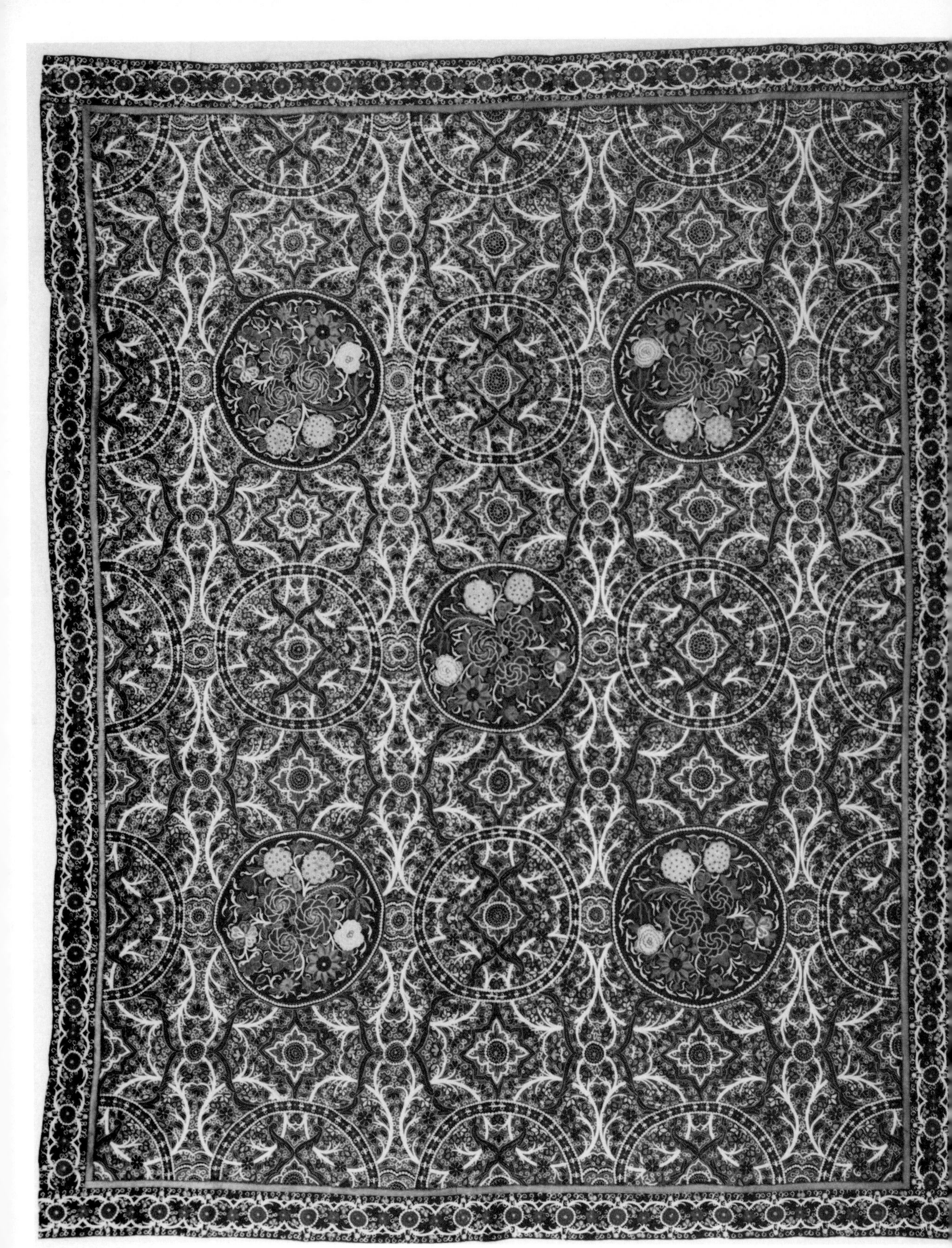

Cat. No. 77.

Cat. No. 78.

Cat. No. 79. ►

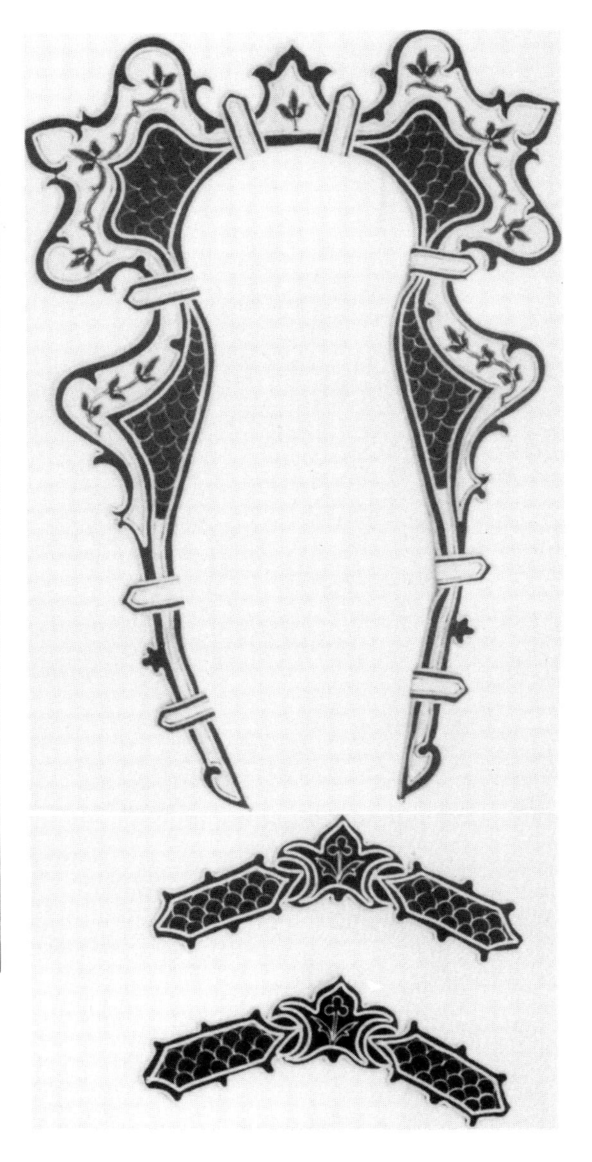

Dohūk
Aleppo
Kirkuk
Hama
SYRIA
Damascus
Baghdād
IRAQ
JORDAN
SAUDI ARABIA
KUWAIT

Fig. 20: Iraq.

IRAQ

Because of the proximity of Iraq to Turkey and Iran, and the great similarity between the ways of life on all sides of the recently established frontiers, such domestic objects as felts are of course to be expected. However, it was much more frequent in the northern mountainous regions than in the hotter plains to the south bordering Syria, Jordan and mainly Saudi Arabia and Kuwait; the hotter climate and fewer sheep probably combine to cause this. Two areas are still noted for their felt today, but, as in other countries, felt-makers are rapidly decreasing in number and the felts being made degenerating in quality and design. Near Dohuk, a few miles south of the Turkish frontier, felt mats are still being made (Cat. No. 82). Made of sheep's wool by the women, they are usually long and narrow with a central pattern in lozenges. The other area in which mats are made is to the east of Dohuk, north of Kirkuk bordering the high mountains of the Zagros, that natural barrier between Iran and Iraq and running up to the Azerbaijan region. Here the high mountain grazing makes it essential for the shepherds to wear the thick felt coats. It is possible that some coats come over the border from Turkey near Mardin.

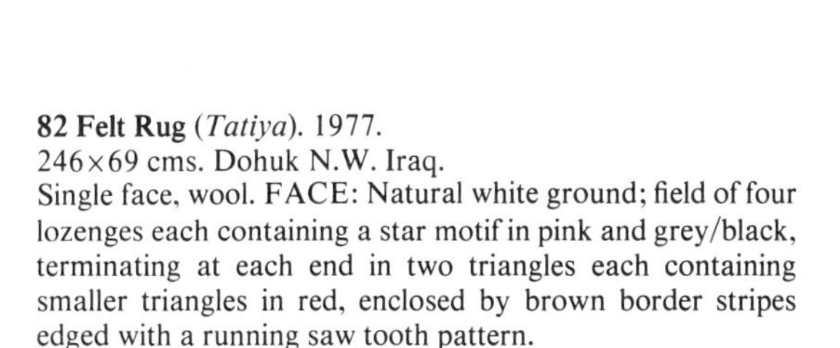

82 Felt Rug (*Tatiya*). 1977.
246×69 cms. Dohuk N.W. Iraq.
Single face, wool. FACE: Natural white ground; field of four lozenges each containing a star motif in pink and grey/black, terminating at each end in two triangles each containing smaller triangles in red, enclosed by brown border stripes edged with a running saw tooth pattern.

These mats are used for sleeping or sitting purposes.

Cat. No. 82.

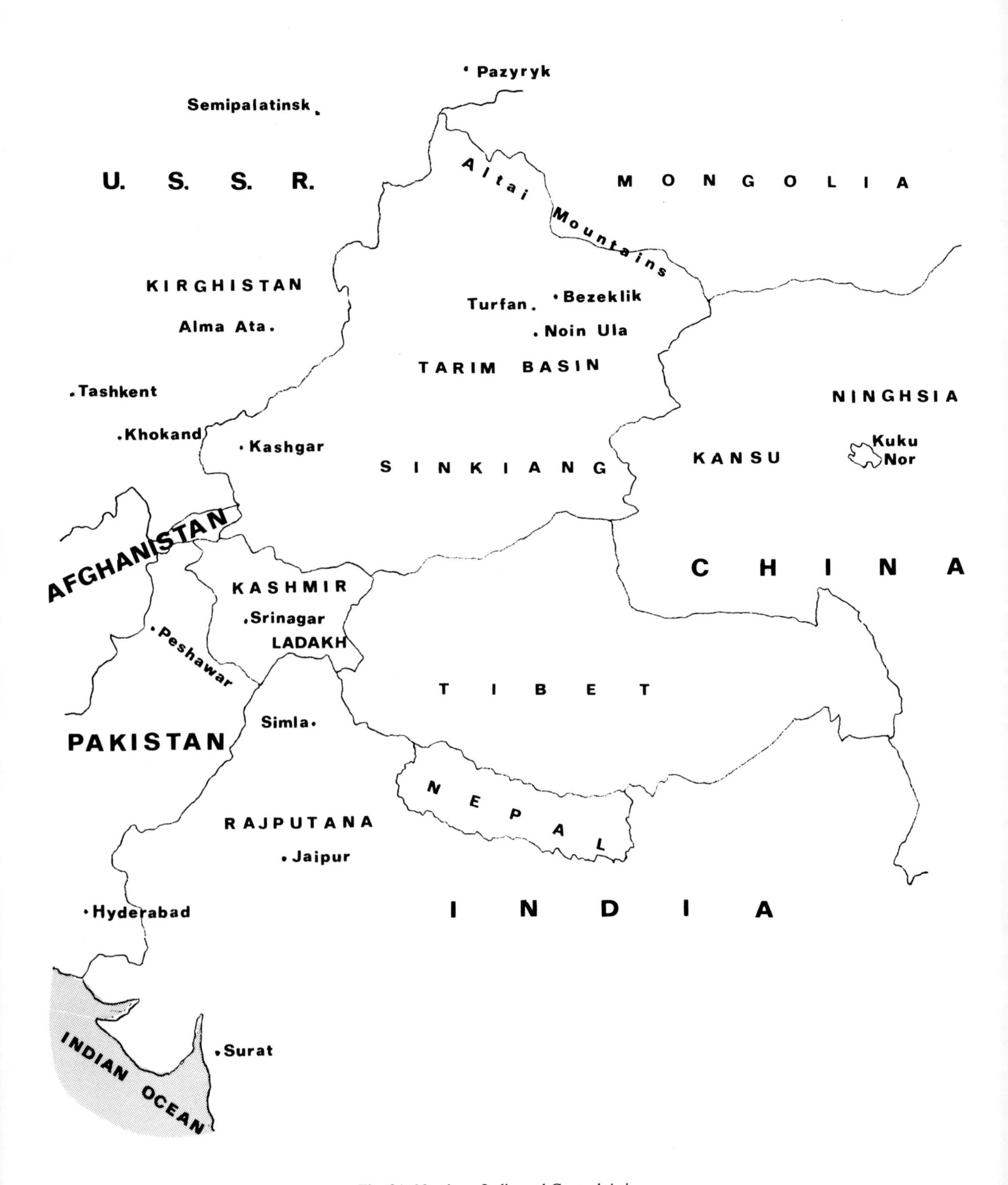

Fig. 21: Northern India and Central Asia.

INDIA

The tradition of felt making in India, first referred to by Strabo (Strabo XV, 1.67) and later in T'ang Annals of the T'ien-pao period, (742-756 A.D.) seems to have steadily continued to the present day. Certainly in the late 17th century, John Fryer travelling from India to Persia (1672-81) noticed at Surat that the houses were covered with 2 or 3 layers of warm felt. Both felted blankets *Kambola* and woven blankets used to be common in India and made in the North and North-West. "At Simla the Kunyts wear felt hats and caps, sometimes with coloured cloths added for decoration" (Watson, 1866). He then mentioned similar felt hats in Central Asia. "The chief of the Kirghiz tribes at Semipalatinsk is said to wear a brown conical hat turned up at the sides, the description indicating a form somewhat like that of the felt 'wide-awake' in use in this country" said Forbes Watson in 1866. He described the larger thick hooded felt cloak common to shepherds throughout "High Asia", and leggings on which coloured wool was used to make surface patterns. He collected an example of the latter at Ladakh, 31 ins×18 ins, weighing 9 ounces and costing 1/-. The end of this plain uncoloured felt was ornamented for the last 6½ ins with coloured silks in diamond stitched patterns. He found cloaks in Jaipur and Rajputana, one embroidered, 1 yd 21 ins×2 yds 21 ins, weighing 3 lbs 13 ozs, the other with a large circular figure formed of fragments of bright coloured cloth pressed into the surface. It was 3 yds×1 yd 20 ins, and weighed 4 lbs 8 ozs. At about the same time descriptions of the mat or *chappar* on which the felt was made came back. It was made of the stems of Guinea grass, bound with thin cords and then crushed. Felt-making with the bow is reported from Srinagar in Kashmir. The bow has long been known there, and is sometimes considered to have come from China (Ågren, 1976, p. 22).

Apart from these tools a very sharp knife was used for "mowing" the surface of the finished felt to an equal level and to bring out the clarity of the pattern. The best felt, *Un,* was made entirely of sheep's wool, but in other types camel and goat hair was also used. Watson pointed out one or two little differences in method e.g. in Peshawar they used the backs of the forearms in the rolling process while others pressed it by foot. Carpets, cushions, bedding, horse-clothing, tent linings and hats were the principal goods made.

In the Chitral valley the nomads still use felt, the most common article being the now woven woollen caps which are felted on the outside to make them warmer (cf. Afghanistan, p. 61).

In the thirties of this century felt industries still flourished in Hyderabad, Jaipur, Ladakh and Rajputana, among other places. In recent years, however, it has been the embroidered mats, *numdah* (the name probably originating from the Persian *namad*) which have survived most generally (Laufer, 1930, pp. 8-10). (Cat. No. 83a, b, 84). Since the last century these have been a popular export to the West. The floral patterns in coloured wools have become more ornate but in many ways remained similar to those of a century ago. In addition a number of small domestic objects were made, such as tea-cosies which were at the end of the last and in this century, favourite presents to take back to England. One from Kashmir is in the exhibition (Cat. No. 85).

Cat. No. 85.

Cat. No. 83(a).

Cat. No. 84.

83 (a) Mat (*Numdah*). 1978.
185×124 cms. Srinagar, Kashmir.
Single face, wool. FACE: Natural ivory ground with four circles of flowers and leaves surrounded by similar motifs in pink, maroon, blue, yellow, brown and black in chain stitch; border of flowers with foliage, enclosed by red chain stitch. Fringe formed by teasing out the felted wool.

(b) Mat (*Numdah*). 1975.
100×76 cms. Srinagar, Kashmir.
Single face, wool. FACE: Natural ivory ground with animals, birds, trees and leaves in grey, brown/red, pink, green, blue and yellow in chain stitch. Border of chain stitch, fringe of ivory wool.

84 Mat (*Numdah*). *c.* 1925.
180×115 cms. Srinagar, Kashmir.
Single face, wool. FACE: Natural ivory ground with birds, trees and flowers in greens, yellows, oranges, pinks, red and brown. Motifs outlined in black chain stitch and infilled with chain stitch in various colours. REVERSE: Shows the back of the face pattern with less detail and cruder stitching, but colours remarkably unfaded. Fringe.

85 Embroidered Tea Cosy *c.* 1948.
29·5×30·5 cms. Peshawar, Kashmir.
Single face, wool. FACE: Natural ivory ground; central field of three irises in light and dark blue, yellow/green and maroon wool chain stitch with borders of maroon and dark brown chain stitch.

AFRICA

Felt is not found in Africa except in those parts influenced by Islam – the province of Ifrikaya (including modern Morocco) in particular (Serjeant, 1951, pp. 82-3); whether felt was made in Morocco before the first Arab invasion we do not know, but the Arab historian, Djāhiz, in 1100 A.D. says that felts were introduced into Morocco in the second century of the Hijra (8th century A.D.), probably from Turkey (Djāhiz, 1937, Vol. 1, p. 366). Another historian, Miskawaihi, informs us that the Byzantine army which besieged Aleppo in 962 A.D. had pavilions (*khārgāhāb*) adorned with felts (*lubud*)* from Magh̲ribi (Morocco). (Miskawaihi, 1920-1, V.210) Djāhiz attests the excellence of Moroccan felts: "The best felts are Chinese, then the red Magh̲ribi variety, then the white Tālikān felts, then the Armenian variety, and then the Khurasan kind (from Persia)". (Djāhiz, 1937, Vol. 1, p. 338). Tha'ālibī also mentions celebrated Moroccan felts.

There were ample sheep, goats and camels to provide wool, and the temperature in the mountains would certainly have justified the use of felt.

We can learn a few details about felt-making from the Arab historians. Al-Sakalī of Malaga says that the felt-maker Muhlāsib always took care that felt was not made from the wool of animals that had died naturally (the smell would indicate this). Nor was coarse wool from the heads of animals to be used. The liquid used in the process of felting was gum, (*ṣamgh*), not starch (*nash̲a*). (Serjeant, 1951, p. 68). Al-Sakalī also

* Lubud — from the Arabic root l-b-d, meaning "stick, adhere, cling, get stuck; cause to adhere and mat together"; labad from the same root means "wool".

Pl. 57: Wall hanging in felted cloth showing prayer alcoves. *Haiti.* 20th century.

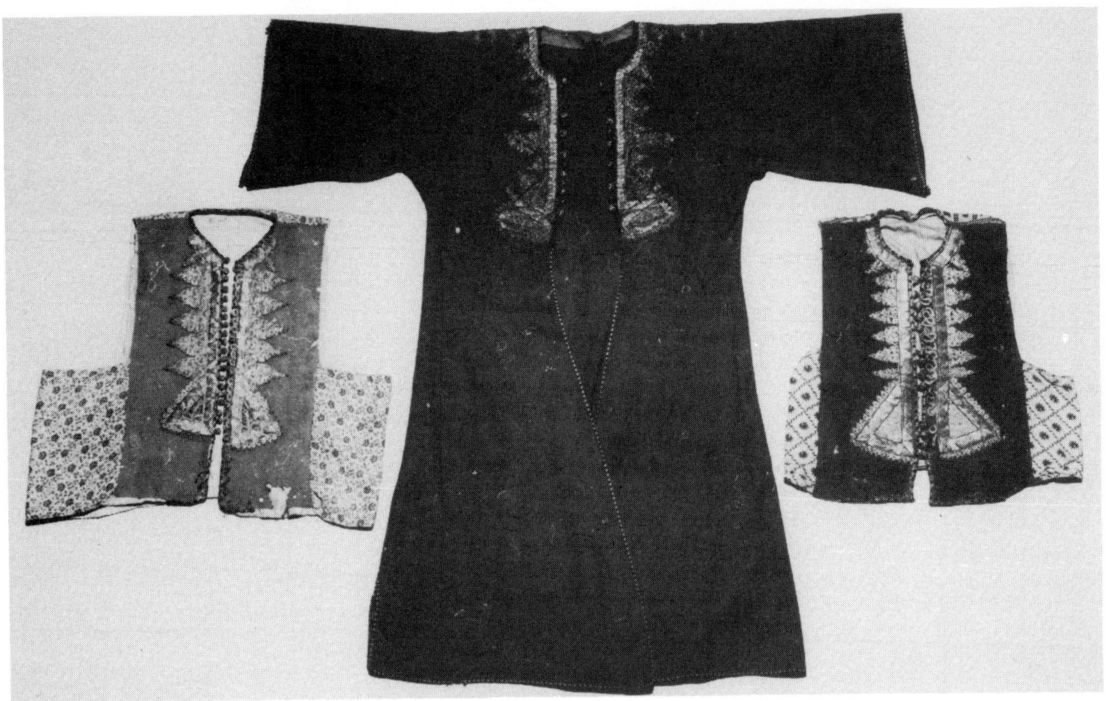

Cat. Nos. 88, 87 and 89.

specifies, as does Ibn Abdūn, the weight, size and quality of the felts. The Egyptian Ma'ālim al-Kurba writes that a trustworthy member of the profession should be placed in charge of felt-makers, and he stresses the high standards which had to be maintained. This particular attention to detail is not found in other Islamic countries where felt was made.

Some time between these references to felt-making in Morocco and the eighteenth century, hand-made felt manufacture disappeared. Under Spanish and French influence, much textile equipment was introduced. (The tradition of felt survives chiefly in the felting of the exterior of woven woollen fabric.)

Before really high-powered machinery came in 25-30 years ago, the felted cloth used to be made in Lyons. If special colours were required, flowers of the right shade were sent to Lyons and the colours copied.

One of the most interesting recently made felt or velvet, or silk objects was a wall-hanging for inside a house and called a *haiti* and used for fêtes and ceremonies by the Berbers (Pl. 57).

The fez used to be worn commonly in Morocco and was made of felt originally but now usually of felted cloth. It has always been referred to as the fez by outsiders, in Morocco it is known as the *tarboosh* (Cat. No. 86). The idea was Turkish. The modern word for felt is *melff* and many of the better kaftans were made out of velvet (*mobra*), both are still plentiful and made at Fez, Tetuan, Cheowan, and elsewhere.

86 Felt hat (*Tarboosh*). 1978.
12·5 cms high × 18 cms diam. (size 4). Tanger.
Machine made, maroon felt hat, stiffened with card and lined in pink fabric with a leather sweat band. On top are three eyelets to serve as air vents and a black synthetic tassel sewn on to the rim.

87 Kaftan *c.* 1930.
119×48·5 cms. Tetuan.
Full length red felted cloth kaftan with central opening and sleeves. Front edges and shoulders decorated with rows of buttons and plaited gold braid. Cuffs and hem edged with binding.

88 Waistcoat Early 20th century.
55×36·5 cms. Tanger.
Lime green felted cloth waistcoat with front opening fastened by decorative buttons in gold braiding and decorated freely in same. Backed by red floral patterned cotton.

89 Waistcoat Early 20th century.
50×40 cms. Tanger.
Red felted cloth waistcoat with front opening, fastened by decorative silver and gold braid and buttons, edged in cotton and gold braid, backed in printed cotton.

SCANDINAVIA

Although there are many references in Norse literature to the widespread use of felt from about 1000 A.D. (Ågren, 1976, p. 7) it has largely died out as a home industry because of the introduction of machines in 1800. *Tova* was the old word used for felt in Norway and Sweden, while in Finland it was known as *huopa*. However, in the extreme north, pockets of felt-making have persisted. In Norway boots (Cat. No. 90) and socks were made although they have imported the stronger thicker versions from Russia – Kola and Archangelsk in particular. Further south in Namdalen, felting was common and since 1950 new home industries sprang up at Mo in Rana, where ready-made factory felt is bought and made up by housewives from already cut pieces. One place further south, without a previous known tradition, has established the industry at Haus, near Bergen. Here Marie Hermundsdal (1815-1908) was instrumental in introducing the techniques. Ivar Aasgård from Bergen, a very good businessman, encouraged the venture so that during and after the First World War many Norwegians made their living from making felt boots and it was even possible for the young to stay in their villages and farms instead of looking for work elsewhere. The working method has not changed much since the boots were first made – by skilful women's hands. To begin with they did not use "forms" on which to shape the boots, which were simply stitched together at the heels. Later, however, the workers found that they could make them by shaping them on a last which they do to this day.

Hats used to be made on some farms on Osterøy, (Pl. 58) and worn by men and women in the 18th century. They were also made on wooden forms. They cost eight pence for a man's and six pence for a woman's hat. A modern version is included in the exhibition (Cat. No. 91).

Pl. 58: Woman with felt hat from Hamre, Osterøy, *c.* 1870.

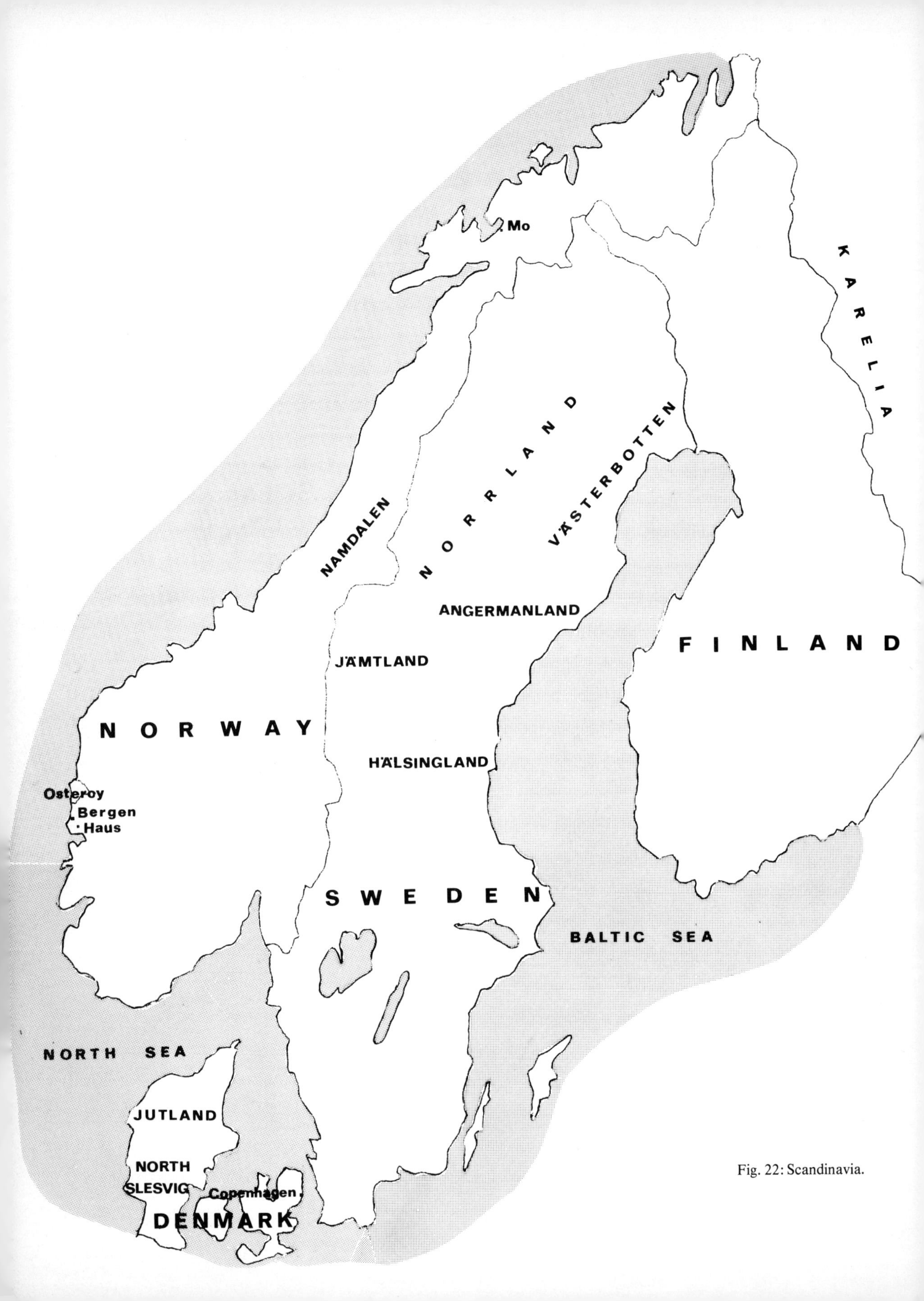

Fig. 22: Scandinavia.

In Sweden the tradition belongs to the Norrland area and did not spread further south than Hälsingland, with its strongest roots in Västerbotten, Jämltand and Ångermanland. Owing to central heating and the introduction of modern materials, the tradition died out until the last war. Then a revival of it making use of local available wool, provided cheap warm socks which proved much warmer on stone floors and as linings for men's boots, working in the forests in sub-zero temperatures. Boots, inner soles, mittens, caps and hats were made but the latter usually in factories. There is also evidence of a Lapp introducing felt-making in Svedjenholmen in about 1900. The Lapps still use felt for its extra warmth.

In Finland the widespread home felt-making industry had died out as a result of a factory being established in 1897 at Kirvu. Felt socks had been used in the cold dry weather but were never as solid as the robust Russian equivalent, imported and known as *labber*. By 1970, six factories were making felt boots and socks. The latter are used by the Finnish army and the former exported to Sweden and Canada. Only one or two felt-makers continue their trade in the North, where the traditions had once been so strong; in the East near Karelen they were working when Katarina Ågren wrote her book on felt-making (1976).

In Lappland traditionally many garments were made of felt; now felted cloth is largely used. In the Exhibition a Lapp costume is shown with some felted cloth ribbons, as well as leather, fur, cotton, embroidery and braid (Cat. No. 92).

Cat. No. 90.

90 Felt Boots 1960.
11·5 cms high×18·5 cms long. Bergen, Norway.
Pair of child's boots with leather soles and trim; metal buckle fastening and slit front.
Made by hand on last in one piece.

91 Felt Hat 1978.
34×37 cms. Osterøy, Norway.
Black felt hat with brim and high crown. Copy of a traditional style of hat used for everyday wear in all weathers in Osterøy into this century.
On loan from Hordamuseet, Stend, Bergen. Made by Øystein Askeland.

92 Lapp Costume 1940.
Smock 102 cms long.
Breeches 90 cms.
Hat 42 cms high.
Woven wool, felted on the exterior (earlier examples would have been made of real felt). Felt is used for trimmings on the smock, hats and breeches.

93 Socks *c.* 1970.
Järvsö, Sweden.
Pair of simple, undecorated, black and white socks made by Karin Lundholm, Järvsö.

94 Gloves *c.* 1970.
Järvsö, Sweden.
Pair of simple, undecorated black and white gloves made by Karin Lundholm, Järvsö.

95 Hat *c.* 1970.
Umeå, Sweden.
Woman's felt embroidered hat, designed by Ulla Böris Matsson, Umeå.

BRITAIN

Felt may have been made in Britain as early as Roman times, whether in a native tradition or brought over by the Romans we cannot be sure. On a sculptured stone found at Housesteads on Hadrian's Wall three hooded figures are shown wearing one-piece garments (probably the *birrus Britannicus*) which would have been made of felt, or felted cloth (Pl. 59).

In the Lake District last century some felt hoods were found while peat-cutting. Unfortunately no firm date could be assigned to them, and the surviving one was sent to the British Museum. We quote H. S. Cowper* on their discovery:

* I am indebted to Mrs. R. Jay for referring me to this book.

"A curious discovery was made in 1867 by men digging peats at Out-Dubs, near the south end of Esthwaite Water. The diggers turned up, some four to six feet below the surface, six large felt bags of conical shape, which are said to have been neatly folded and laid one upon the other. At the time there appears to have been no one in the district who took any interest in the find, and the writer only heard of it about 1884, when all had been lost except one, which is now in his possession. It is made of soft warm felt, brown in colour (but this may be due to peat stain), and when laid out flat, about two feet wide at the widest part, and about one foot seven inches in length. This has been exhibited at the Society of Antiquaries, at the British Association and elsewhere; and though various suggestions have been made, the best is that they are

Pl. 59: Three hooded figures carved in stone, wearing cloaks. Housesteads, probably 3rd century A.D.

hoods of primitive manufacture. Such finds are rare, but not unknown . . .". (H. S. Cowper, 1899, pp. 135 ff.).

". . . but whether they belong to a very early date or the Middle Ages, has never been decided. All seem now lost save one, which I placed in the British Museum . . .". (Fig. 23). (H. S. Cowper, 1928, p. 68).

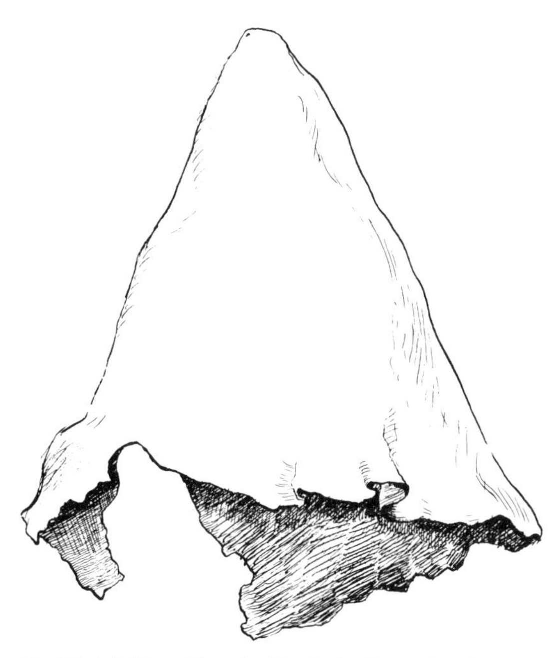

Fig. 23: A felt hood found at Out Dubs, Lancashire, in 1867.

The manufacture of felt hats has continued in Britain, in particular in the north-west, for centuries. Miss P. M. Giles, M.A. made a special study of the earlier history of the industry, from which we quote the following extract:

> "The manufacture, which was carried out almost entirely by hand, therefore into 3 main stages; preparation of raw materials, making, and finishing. Wool had to be cleaned, carded, and cut into lengths suitable for felting. The various types of fur: beaver or its substitutes (seal-wool after 1810, monkey stuff or nutria from the South American Coypus, or sometimes ostrich down); red wool from Peru, camel-hair, goat-hair, rabbits' and hares' fur, all had to be sheared from the skins. The fur was then cleaned, graded, and coarse hairs known as kemps, removed. This was a slow job, performed by women in the North (see *A Six Months Tour through the North of England 1771*, III, 191) and was in fact one of the first to be mechanized by a machine called a blower. In 1821 the firm of Messrs T. W. & J. Christy & Co. applied steam-power to their machine; even so, for the spring trade the material could not be prepared speedily enough and the blower was at work night and day. After preparation the materials for a given number of hats were measured out by weight to the workmen. Making was commenced in a room called a bow-garret. Here a long table was partitioned by hurdles; at each section a man worked an instrument called a bow over the pile of fur and wool. This bow, of deal wood, was suspended from the ceiling, held in the left hand, and the catgut bowstring plucked with a wooden pin. The vibration caused the fur to scatter and settle in a thin even layer, the fibres distributed as much as possible in every direction. The superior quality nap or ruffing was separately worked with a lighter bow and finer catgut.
>
> The layer of fur was formed into a batt, made firm by hand, or, in the case of beaver, by the pressure of a piece of osier work called a gathering-basket. Another batt separated by a wet cloth, was then laid over the first, to form a conical hood. The slightly larger hood of napping was then applied at this stage in all but plated hats." (Giles, 1959).

She goes on to describe the processes of shaping and shrinking the hats to the right size.

The following information on the modern manufacture of felt hats – from fur and wool – has been supplied by Dr. T. Barr, Director of Research, Associated British Hat Manufacturers Ltd., Stockport:

FUR-FELT HAT MANUFACTURE

The manufacture of felt hats in this country has continued for over 500 years as evidenced by the history of the Worshipful Company of Feltmakers of London, a guild company set up for the control and protection of the industry. This company was incorporated by Charter under James I on 2nd August, 1604, but chronicles show that it was an active craft prior to that date. The Haberdashers Company history records the fact that it was united with the Hatters & Furriers on 7th April, 1501. The Art and Mystery of Feltmaking must therefore have been an established craft in the 15th century, most likely as a cottage industry widely spread over the country. Today there remain only two centres of felt hat manufacture from raw material to finished hat – wool-felt manufacture in Atherstone, Warwickshire and fur-felt manufacture in the Manchester area.

In spite of mechanization and the application of scientific principles, fur-felt hat manufacture is still, in part, a craft industry relying on the skill and judgement of the operative. Although hare's fur is used for special finishes, the main raw material is rabbit fur which is prepared by Hatters' Fur Manufacturers. The rabbit has two distinctive coats, an undercoat of fine fur, and an outer coat of coarse guard hairs. The first stage in manufacture is to remove the guard hairs mechanically, leaving the desired fine fur which, to assist the

felting properties, is chemically treated on the skin so that the reaction is confined to the fibre tips. After stoving and conditioning, the pelt, which goes for glue manufacture, is shredded from the fur.

The hat manufacturer buys ready prepared the fur of either wild or tame rabbits. The wild fur is classified according to the season the skins are collected, e.g. winter skins. The tame fur is bought according to its colour: white, through grey, to black, or mixed. The first operation is to select and mix the different furs to correspond with the final colour of the finished hats, a white fur for pastel shades, a light to medium blend for intermediate shades and dark coloured blends for full to dark shades.

The mixture of furs is charged into a large rotating drum to give an intimate blend of the component parts and then passes through a conical separator which removes contaminating sand and skin pieces left from the cutting. Finally the fur is passed through a multichamber blowing machine where it is subjected to successive air currents which further cleanse the fur by removing residual unwanted guard hairs.

The felt manufacture commences by mechanically delivering an accurately weighed quantity of fur in a controlled air stream on to a revolving perforated cone on a forming machine, (Pl. 60), which is sprayed with water to give cohesion to the fur. The form is skilfully peeled off and assembled in batches of 6-8 depending on the weight, wrapped in a cloth and subjected to a mild mechanical action in a "hardening" machine to give an initial knitting together of the fur fibre and the beginning of felting (Pl. 61). "Settling" is carried out similarly with increased mechanical action to accelerate the felting and produce a form of sufficient strength to withstand, unprotected, the more severe mechanical action of the main felting multi-roller machines. Again this is a two stage process of mild and of increased severity of action. As the name implies the machine consists of two horizontal banks of rollers, say nine on top and ten on the bottom bank. These subject the forms to a traversing action which carries them through the machine where they are subjected to alternate pressure and relaxation and at the same time to an intermittent shearing action due to the oscillation of the rollers in a direction parallel to their axis, commonly referred to as "jig". In the final stage the difference in severity of action stems from an increase in the pressure and in the frequency and amplitude of the jig.

Pl. 60: Forming machine where fur is deposited on a perforated cone.

Pl. 61: Hardening machine where the forms are rolled in a cloth and subjected to mild mechanical action.

Pl. 62: Mounting the felted bodies on a perforated metal cone for dyeing.

The felting is carried out in these machines under a constant spray of boiling acidulated water to assist the felting. The forms are fed into the machines individually according to a well defined pattern in order to preserve their conical shape, and the position of the leading edge is changed – by "crozing" – to prevent the formation of thick places called "welts". These machines complete the felting and from a form when flat, originally 25 ins high by 30 ins across the base, produce a fully felted "body" 10 ins by 15 ins and of considerable strength.

The bodies produced are dyed in an open beck or, more commonly, in a cone-dyeing machine (Pl. 62) in which the liquor is pumped through the felt – a method which overcomes penetration problems associated with the former. The dyed bodies, after drying, are proofed in the brim area with a borax solution/emulsion of shellac to give stiffness and shape retention in the hat, (Pl. 63).

From this point the shaping of the hat begins by partial opening out of the brim – "brim breaking" – in one machine, and rounding of the crown region – "tip stretching" – in a separate machine. The hat is then blocked to an approximation of the final shape with a sharp delineation of brim to crown, (Pl. 64, 65). Whilst special surface finishes of the felt are produced, such as raised finishes, melusines and other finishes, the majority of hats are sandpapered on specially designed machines to give smooth flat finishes to the crown and brim – "pouncing". The final hat shape is produced by pressing the crown and flanging the brim to the correct curl.

Trimming, which adds the sweat band, the ribbons and lining, produces the final article for sale to the customer.

WOOL-FELT HAT MANUFACTURE

A typical blend for the manufacture of wool-felt hats would be approximately 20% wool and 80% wool noils (the short fibre from combed wool) of a fine quality.

The material is fed to a hatter's card and emerges as a fine web of fibres which is wound on to a double cone which, in addition to its rotational motion, has a reciprocating action in a horizontal plane pivotting

Pl. 63: Proofing: brims are impregnated with shellac preparation.

Pl. 64: Steam blocking, where the bodies are steamed and forced on to a wooden block.

Pl. 65: Gas blocking, where the body is pulled over a gas-heated metal block.

about a central vertical axis. When the correct weight is judged to have been applied the double form is cut centrally to give two similar conical forms. The form of loose fibres is placed over a cone and a vibrating arm hardens the tip region. An interliner is placed inside the form which is hardened on a plate hardening machine, a steam heated chest on to which a vibrating shoe is engaged under a loading spring. These combined processes produce a thin hardened form of sufficient strength to be felted on a multi-roller machine to a given stage. The settled forms are then fed, in bulk, to a specially shaped receptacle and are bumped by hammers which may be of the falling type where the load is applied gravitationally or fixed thrust hammers where the load is applied mechanically. At the half way stage the forms are removed and dyed in open beck machines then returned for colour bumping.

When the bodies are fully felted they are proofed with shellac, as for fur felt, except that in addition to brim proofing the crowns are also wash proofed with a weaker proofing liquor.

The subsequent stretching and finishing processes are similar to those for fur-felt.*

* The Felt-hatting Industry in Czechoslovakia.

There is a long tradition of making felt (*plsti*) in Czechoslovakia. Hats of both wool- and fur-felt were made by hand. The oldest record of felt hats is to be found in the wood-carvings of St. Egidus' church, Bardějov, Slovakia (c. 1418-1444), where men are depicted wearing hats of varying styles.

A variety of tools was used in the production of felt, including a bow, which was struck by a wooden pin, as in British examples; carding apparatus; wooden blocks for shaping the crown and brim of hats. (cf. p. 105).

Early on, the felt-hatting industry was organised in guilds, with a rigorous examination leading to the status of Master Craftsman. A family might have a history of felt-making which lasted several generations. Hand-made felt declined in use after the introduction of mechanisation in the 19th Century. Today machine-made felt hats – of hare and rabbit fur – continue to be made.
(Fig. 24).

Fig. 24: Czech hats of the 17th and 18th centuries.

96 Hatter's Bow *c.* 1850.
l. 241 cms. Stockport.
Ash shaft and sounding board, strung with gut, and struck with a wooden pin. Bows were replaced by mechanical processes in the 1880s. Made for Christy & Co. Ltd., (now Associated British Hat Manufacturers).

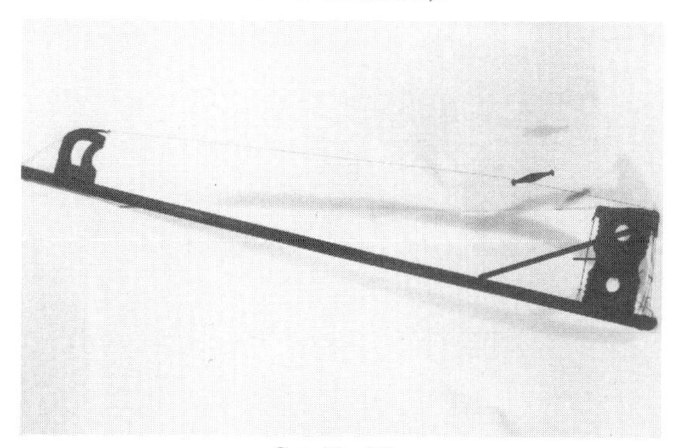

Cat. No. 96.

97 Hatter's Block.
Size $8\frac{1}{2}$. Stockport.
Felt-covered hat block made for the Chief Constable of Shrewsbury. It is two sizes larger than average.
Series of hat blocks, of sycamore or alder as above, each of a different size, would be used for the "ready-made" market. Those requiring made-to-measure hats might have had an individual hat block, but more likely a conform.

98 Conforms. 19th-20th century.
Stockport.
(a) The King of Siam. 18·5×16 cms.
(b) H.R.H. Prince Albrecht of Prussia. 19×16 cms.
(c) H.M. King George V. 19×14·5 cms.
(d) The Crown Prince of Sweden. 19×16 cms.
(e) His Imperial Highness, The Grand Duke of Russia. 20·5×16 cms.
The head is measured with a conformateur, from which a conform is made. Each conform is made up of layers of card reinforced with gossamer and coated with shellac and is used to record the exact shape of a section through the head in the manufacture of made-to-measure hats.

100 Samples of Blended Fur.
(a) Petit Bon. Unlocked.
(b) FJ. Blend. Blown.
(c) Petit Bon. Part Blown.
(d) Jardinier. Part Blown.
(e) Bariolé. Part Blown.
(f) Kemps. Part Blown.
(g) White Fur. Unlocked.
The different furs are selected and mixed to correspond with the final colour of the finished hats, blended and passed through a blowing machine to remove unwanted guard hairs.

101 (a), (b). Felt Samples in "Settled" Form.
Settling is carried out with mechanical action to accelerate the felting process and harden/strengthen the fibres to withstand further processes.

102 Four Stages in Hat Manufacture.
(a) Dyed body: conical form, brown (27·5 cms circ.). Bodies are dyed in a cone-dyeing machine in which the liquor is pumped through into the felt.
(b) Fully felted body. Conical form, grey.
(c) Blocked body, brown. Hats are blocked into shape approximately with a sharp delineation of brim to crown.
(d) Hat showing pounced and pressed shape.

Although in general felt making seems to be a declining industry, in Scandinavia and also in Britain it is being taken up again by craftsmen, including one living locally. Mrs. Short of Kirkby Lonsdale was studying textiles at Liverpool Polytechnic in 1972 when she visited the "Turcoman of Iran" exhibition (arranged by Abbot Hall Art Gallery in conjunction with the Whitworth Art Gallery, Manchester), where a complete *yurt* and several items of felt were displayed; her fascination with the felts led her to experiment making felt for herself. With the encouragement of her college, and the industrial felt-makers, Bury and Masco, Rossendale, she began making felts, both with the aid of the industrial process, and by hand (in a manner very similar to that described in Chapter One).

EXHIBITS BY PAT SHORT

A. Felts Produced Wholly or Partly by Industrial Processes.

Samples

103 220×58 cms, produced at Bury and Masco. A sample of needle-felt using blended natural colours of wool (from S. Africa, as in most of the other British exhibits). This sample has a high proportion of *kemp* (white, dead fibres of wool in the fleece, without scales, and therefore not taking part in the felting process). Colour of this sample predominantly dark brown.

104 (a)-(g) were produced at the International Wool Secretariat, Ilkley; in all these, a background of white needle-felt is used, of a standard width; this white felt is produced by needle-punching woollen fibres on to a nylon/cotton scrim; pieces of wool are then dropped by hand on to the surface in the desired pattern and needle-punched again.

(a) 72 ×35 cms. Natural Berber wools, in a variety of colours, including dark-brown and off-white, have been needle-punched on to the white background.

(b) 48×36 cms. Natural ginger wool needle-punched on.

(c) 72×36 cms. An overlay of tones of beige and grey.

(d) 47×36 cms. Dyed wool, mainly red and orange in a finer and smoother appliqué than (a)-(c).

Nos. (e)-(g) were conceived as wall-hangings.

(e) 78×36 cms. Overlay of lumps of wool and threads, in muted shades of purple, pink, cream, blue and green.

(f) 77×36 cms. Similar to (e) – overlay in wool and threads of blue, mauve, yellow and brown.

(g) 288×36 cms. Overlay of fine lumps of green, red, turquoise, blue and yellow wools.

Cat. No. 105.

105 cf. 101. Industrially-made felt, made up in peasant-style coat.

B. Hand-felted Articles.

106 (a) House-boots.
28×22 cms. in white wool, with red embroidery.
(b) House-boots.
31×21 cms in natural, dark-brown, and off-white wool.

107 Cushion.
38 cms square. Mottled dark brown and off-white wool.

108 Rug.
116×104 cms, irregular-sided square. White background, felted over with black (with kemp. cf. 101), dark brown and grey wool.

109 (a) Sample.
123×60 cms. Thick, soft white felt, with embroidery wool in three greys. (This wool is particularly white, having been *scoured,* i.e. washed with detergent, to remove particles of vegetable matter from the fleece.)
(b) Wall-hanging: Foundation.
153×81 cms. White textured wool background, overlaid with motif in dark-brown wool.

110 Bolero.
Dusky pink wool, stitched together from four separate pieces of felt, and embroidered with spirals in white wool; lined with cotton.

111 (a) Hanging.
30×24 cms. Garden, embroidered on white wool felt ground, with green felt overlaid.
(b) Hanging.
32×30 cms. Garden, embroidered on a white wool felt ground, overlaid with green and blue.

EXHIBITS BY PETER CHORLEY

112 (a) Hanging.
115×80 cms. Composition of brown felt.
(b) Hanging.
100×80 cms. Composition of brown felt.

Cat. No. 110.

Cat. No. 106(a).

DYES USED IN FELT MAKING

The shades of colour derived from the traditional plant products used by the dyers depend on a variety of factors, such as the type of mordant, the acidity or alkalinity of the fluid, the chemical content of the local water and the temperature. Even the age of the plant might affect the final result. The vegetable dyes mellow gently to attractive shades and lack the harshness which is such a disagreeable feature of modern synthetic colours.

They used very few ingredients to make their colours: the skill was in mordanting and blending. The dye-bath was often used again after the first dyeing which resulted in a paler version of the same colour. Sometimes they re-used the dye-bath three or four times. It was also possible to mordant the wool with different mordants, immerse it all in the same dye-bath and it would come out in different colours according to the mordant. This was known to Pliny who described it vividly in his Natural History.

Oriental vegetable dyes were largely supplanted after 1856 by synthetic dyes introduced from the West. These arrived in the larger urban centres first and finally reached the villages and nomads. The synthetic dyes were of course easier to use and did not require the time-consuming collecting of natural materials, and the grinding and preparation sometimes necessary. In the first few years the new dyes faded and ran, but these difficulties were later overcome and, eventually, synthetic dyes have come to be used extensively.

Some natural dyes used in felt from a selection of regions

S. Turkey – Antalya area (cf. Landreau, 1978, pp. 32-5)

Colour	*Source*
red	madder root (till 20 years ago) or kermes
sunflower yellow	milkweed or spurge (euphorbia) *sutleghen*
navy blue	barley yeast plus root dye – indigo

Afghanistan – Uzbek textiles (Lindahl & Knorr, 1975, p. 72)

Colour	*Source*
greenish-yellow	mulberry tree algae (*tukhmak*)
sulphur-yellow	larkspur (*isparak*)
black	gall nut of pistachio tree (*abuzgunta*) or pomegranate rind
blue	indigo plant (*nil*)
red	cochineal (*kyrmisi*) or henna or rujan (*krapp*)
faded purple	logwood

USSR – Turkestan (Beresneva, 1976, p. 6)

Colour	*Source*
red, reddish-purple, deep cherry, pink	madder root
yellow	buckthorn berries, *sary-chop* grass
beige, brown	pomegranate rind
green	copper filings treated with sour milk or vinegar

Imported dyes – e.g. cochineal, indigo – used sparingly because expensive.

Iran (Information supplied by F. Darrehshouri)
An attempt is being made by the Tribal School of Crafts to re-introduce the following dyes, which have declined in use due to the introduction of chemical dyes.

Colour	*Source*
red	the flower *Norouz goule* (means 'New Year')
green	leaves from the bush *Mōrdar ăchăche*
yellow	sweet pomegranate rind (*anar*)

BIBLIOGRAPHY

Abbot Hall Art Gallery, Kendal. (1971).
The Turcoman of Iran. Ed. M. E. Burkett, Titus Wilson, Kendal.

Ågren, Katarina. (1976).
Tovning. ICA-Förlaget AB, Västerås.

Andrews, P. A. (1973).
"The White House of Khurasan: The Felt Tents of the Iranian Yomut and Gökleñ." *Iran.* B.I.P.S., Vol. XI. (1973) pp. 93-110.

Asahi. (1962).
"Treasures of the Shosoin." Article on the Shosoin at Nara, printed in a Japanese newspaper called *A Sayi-Shinbun.* Northern Section Publishing Company, Tokyo, Japan.

Barnett, R. D. (1953 and 1955).
"The World's Oldest Persian Carpet, preserved for 2400 years in perpetual ice in Central Siberia." *The Illustrated London News,* 11 July 1953 and 1 January 1955.

Beaumont, Robert. (1924).
Carpets and Rugs. Benn.

Bellew, H. W. (1862).
Journal of a Political Mission to Afghanistan. pp. 10, 31, 320, 351, 441 (for references to felt). Smith, Elder & Co., London.

Bellinger, Louise. (1962).
"Textiles from Gordion." *The Bulletin of the Needle and Bobbin Club.* 45, nos. 1-2, pp. 5-34. U.S.A.

Benjamin, S. O. W. (1887).
Persia and the Persians. John Murray, London.

Beresneva, L. (1976).
The Decorative and Applied Art of Turkomenia. Aurora Art Publishers, Leningrad.

Bidder, Hans. (1964).
Carpets from Eastern Turkestan, known as Khotan, Samarkand and Kansu Carpets. Zwemmer, London.

Birdwood, G. C. M. (1880).
Industrial Arts of India, (Tabriz Felts p. 134), Chapman & Hall, London.

Brudvik, L. (1970)
"Ullskoen frå Haus", Norsk Husflid, No. 1, pp. 2-3, Grøndahl & Søn, Oslo.

Burkett, M. E. (1977).
"An Early Date for the Origin of Felt." *Anatolian Studies.* Vol. XXVII (1977), pp. 111-115 B.I.A.A.

Carpini, Johannes de Plano.
Voyage into the North East Part of the World, in the year of our Lord 1246.
Historia Mongolorum (1900). Hakluyt Society, London.

Central Office of Popular Art. (1975).
Czech Folk Art Production. Prague.

Clark, Hartley. (1922).
Bokhara, Turkoman and Afghan Rugs. John Lane, London.

Chardin, Sir John. (1686).
The Travels of Sir John Chardin into Persia and the East Indies .... For Moses Pitt, London.

C.I.B.A. Reviews.
"Felt" 1958/11.
"Dress in Roman and Later Times for Travel" 1962/3.
"The Diverse forms of Textile Fabrics" 1965/1.

Cook, Gordon J. (1968).
A Handbook of Textile Fibres, 4th ed. Merrow Publishing Co.

Cowper, H. S.
Hawkshead (1899) Bemrose & Sons Ltd., London.
Hawkshead & Neighbourhood (1928) 2nd ed. Titus Wilson, Kendal.

Djāhiz. (1937).
Nihayāt al-Arab fī Funūm āl-Adab. Nuwairi, Cairo.

Edwards, A. Cecil. (1953).
The Persian Carpet. Duckworth, London.

Emery, I. (1966).
The Primary Structure of Fabrics. Textile Museum, Washington.

Forbes, R. J. (1955-58).
Studies in Ancient Technology. 6 vols. Leiden.

Friedlander, Ira. (1975).
The Whirling Dervishes. Wildwood House, London.

Gervers-Molnár, Veronika. (1973).
The Hungarian Szür. An Archaic Mantle of Eurasian Origin. Royal Ontario Museum.

Gervers, Veronika. (1974).
"Methods of Traditional Felt-Making in Anatolia and Iran." *Bulletin de Liaison de Centre International D'Etude des Textiles Anciens.* Lyon.

Gervers, Michael and Veronika. (1974).
"Felt-making Craftsmen of the Anatolian and Iranian Plateaux." *Textile Museum Journal,* Washington Vol. iv. no. 1. pp. 14-29.

Giles, P. M. (1959).
"The Felt-Hatting Industry, *c.* 1500-1850, with special reference to Lancashire and Cheshire." Reprinted in *Transactions of the Lancashire and Cheshire Antiquarian Society.* Vol. LXIX.

Goldsmid, Sir F. J. (1876) (quoting Major Beresford Lovett – 1870-71).
Eastern Persia 1870-72: An Account of the Journeys of the Persian Boundary Commission. Introduction by J. Goldsmid. MacMillan.

Hackes, Hermann. (1960).
Oriental Rugs – an Illustrated Guide. London.

Hakluyt, R. (1903).
"R. Hakluyt's Principal Navigations." *Hakluyt Society* Extra Series Vol. 1, pp. 135-137, 142-144, 234. Glasgow.

Hansman, John. (1968).
"The Problems of Qūmis." *Journal of the Royal Asiatic Society,* 1968, pp. 111-139.

Hansman, John and Stronach, David. (1970).
"A Sasanian Repository at Shahr-i-Qūmis." *Journal of the Royal Asiatic Society,* 1970, pp. 142-155.

Harada, J. (1932).
English Catalogue of Treasure in the Imperial Repository, Shosoin. Tokyo.

Herodotus.
The Histories. (1958) (Translation by Aubrey de Sélincourt.) Penguin Books.

Jettmar, K. (1967).
Art of the Steppes. (Translation of *Kunst der Welt: Die Frühen Steppenvölken,* 1964, tr. Ann E. Keep.) Crown Publishers, New York.

Karlsen, I. (1977).
"Laddetoving", *Norsk Husflid,* No. 1, pp. 6-8 Grøndahl & Søn, Oslo.

King, Peter. (1966).
Afghanistan Cockpit in High Asia. Geoffrey Bles, London.

Krist, G. (1938).
Alone through the Forbidden Lands. Faber & Faber.

Landreau, Anthony. (Ed). (1978).
Yörük, the Nomadic Weaving Tradition of the Middle East. Museum of Art, Carnegie Institute, Pittsburgh.

Laszlo, G. (1944).
A honfoglalo Magyar nép élete. (Life of the Hungarian people at the time of their settling in Hungary in the 9th cent.) Budapest.

Laufer, Berthold. (1930).
"The Early History of Felt." *American Anthropologist* New Series. 32, no. 1. pp. 1-18.

Le Strange, G. (1966).
Lands of the Eastern Caliphate. Frank Cass & Co. Ltd., London.

Lindahl, D. and Knorr, T. (1975).
Uzbek Exhibition Catalogue. Basel.

Lubell, Cecil (Editor). (1976).
Textile Collections of the World. Studio Vista, New York.

Lumsden, H. B. (1860).
Mission to Kandahar. Baptist Mission Press, Calcutta.

McGovern, W. M. (1939).
The Early Empires of Central Asia. Chapel Hill.

Maillart, Ella. (1942).
Cruises and Caravans. Dent, London.

Marvin, Charles. (1881).
Merv, the Queen of the World; and the scourge of the man-stealing Turcomans. W. H. Allen & Co. London.

Meister, W. (1931-36).
"Zur Geschichte des Filzteppichs im. 1. Jahrtausend n. Chr." *Ostasiatische Zeitschrift.* Neue Folge, Vols. 10 & 12, 47-61. Berlin.

Mellaart, James. (1966).
(1) "Excavations at Çatal Hüyük 1965." *Sonderdruck aus Archäologischer Anzeiger.* Heft. 1. pp. 1-15. Verlag Walter de Groyter & Co. Berlin.
(2) "Excavations at Çatal Hüyük 1965." Fourth Preliminary Report. *Anatolian Studies XVI* (1966). pp. 165-91, B.I.A.A.

Metropolitan Museum, New York. (1976).
From the Lands of the Scythians. Exhibition Catalogue. Metropolitan Museum of Art, The Los Angeles County Museum of Art.

Meyer, F. S. (1924).
A Handbook of Ornament. Emil Stephen, Leipzig.

Michaud, Roland and Sabrina. (1977).
Caravanes de Tartarie. Chêne, Paris.

Miskawaihi. (1920-21).
The Eclipse of the Abbasid Caliphate. Translated by H. F. Amedroz and D. S. Margolionth. Oxford.

O'Donovan, E. (1882).
The Merv Oasis .... Vol 1, pp. 173-4, 208, 217, 227, 267, 429. Smith, Elder & Co. London.

Oliphant, L. (1953).
Russian Shores of the Black Sea. Wm. Blackwood and Sons, London.

Perkins, Dexter, Jnr. (1969).
"The Fauna of Çatal Hüyük." *Science,* 24 April, 1969.

Phillips, E. D. (1965).
The Royal Hordes, Nomad Peoples of the Steppes. Thames and Hudson, London.

Pliny. (1964).
Natural History, Ed. J. Newsome. Oxford.

Polar, Dr. J. E. (1891).
Catalogue of the Vienna Exhibition of Oriental Carpets 1891. pp. 33-5, 87. Vienna.

Pope, A. U. and Ackerman, P. (1938).
A Survey of Persian Art from Prehistoric Times to the Present. (Vols. I-VII).

Ackerman, P. (1960).
"Verethraghna Avatars on the Shosoin Painted Screen Panels." *Op. cit.* Vol. XV, pp. 3286-3295.

Hayashi, Ryoichi. (1960).
"The Iranian Animal Style on Treasures of the Shosoin Repository." *Op. cit.* Vol. XV, pp. 3275-3285.

Mostafavi, M. T. (1960).
"Note on Persian Art at the Shosoin." *Op. cit.* Vol. XV, pp. 3265-3267.

Sudzuki, Osamu. (1960).
"Horse Furniture in the Shosoin Repository – Iranian Influences & Japanese Variations." *Op. cit.* Vol. XV, pp. 3296-3310.
Asia Institute of Pahlavi University, Iran.

Preece, J. R. (1894).
In: *Diplomatic Consular Reports, Persia, 1892-3.* No. 1376. Isfahan Report, Foreign Office.

Purce, Jill. (1974).
The Mystic Spiral, Journey of the Soul. Thames and Hudson, London.

Redard, Georges. (1974).
Afghanistan. Edition Silva-Zurich.

Rice, T. Talbot.
The Scythians (1958). *The Seljuks* (1961). Thames and Hudson, London.

Rubruck, Friar William of, (1900).
The Journey of William of Rubruck, trans. & ed. W. W. Rockhill. Hakluyt Society, London.

Rudenko, Sergei I. (1970).
Frozen Tombs of Siberia: The Pazyryk Burials of Iron-Age Horsemen. J. M. Dent & Sons, London. (Trans. Dr. M. W. Thompson of *Kultura Naseleniya Gornogo Altaya v Skifskoe Vremya,* 1953. Academy of Sciences of the U.S.S.R.)

Ryder, M. L. (1964).
"The History of Sheep Breeds in Britain." *The Agricultural History Review.* Vol. XII, pt. 1.

Scarce, Jennifer. (1976).
"Isfahan in Camera – 19th Century Persia Through the Photographs of Ernst Höltzer." *AARP – Art and Archaeology Research Papers.* April 1976. London.

Serjeant, R. B. (1951).
"Material for a History of Islamic Textiles up to the Mongol Conquest." *Ars Islamica.* Vols. 15-16.

Seton Lloyd and Mellaart, J. (1962).
Beycesultan, Vols. I-III. British Institute of Archaeology, Ankara. London.

Sinor, E. Denis. (1963).
"The Making of Felt." *Aspects of Altaic Civilization of the Uralic and Altaic Series.* Vol. 23. From proceedings of the 5th Meeting of the Permanent International Altaic Conference held at Indiana University (June 4-9, 1962). Indiana University Publications.

Smith, Captain John. (1630).
True Travels, Adventures and Observations in Europe, Asia, Africa and America from 1593-1629. London.

Stark, Freya. (1970).
The Minaret of Djam. John Murray, London.

Stein, Sir Aurel.
Sand Buried Ruins of Khotan (1903). T. F. Unwin. *Ancient Khotan* (1907). Vols. I & II. Oxford. *Ruins of Desert Cathay* (1912). Vol. 1. MacMillan. *Serindia: The Niya Site* (detailed report of the explorations in Central Asia and Westernmost China) (1921). 3 vols. Oxford. *Innermost Asia* (1928.) Vols. I-III. Oxford.

Street, Lucie. (1967).
The Tent Pegs of Heaven. Robert Hale, London.

Tomlinson, Charles. (Ed.) (1854).
Tomlinson's Cyclopaedia of Useful Arts and Manufactures. George Virtue & Co. London & New York.

Toynbee, Arnold. (1973).
Constantine Porphyrogenitus and his World. Oxford.

Trever, Camilla. (1932).
Excavations in Northern Mongolia (1924-25). pp. 31, 33, 41, 56, 58, 60, 62, 67, 71. Leningrad.

Tsarageli, D. (1972).
Georgian Decorative Thick Felts. Khelovneba Publishing House, Tblisi.

Von le Coq, A. (1916).
Volkskundliches aus Ost-Turkestan with contribution from O. von Falke: Ch. VII "Filzteppiche aus Kutschā". pp. 29, 30, 33. Berlin.

Von Schwarz, Frans. (1900).
Turkestan. Freiburg.

Watson, J. Forbes. (1866).
Textile Manufactures and the Costumes of the People of India. London.

Weyns, Dr. (1960).
"Kempische Zandtekeningen." *Ars Folklorica.* Belgium.

Whitworth Art Gallery, Manchester. (1976).
The Qashqā'i of Iran Section F, Felts, pp. 61-3, by M. E. Burkett. Whitworth Art Gallery, Manchester.

Wiet. (1959).
Arabica. p. 21.

Wild, J. P. (1970).
Textile Manufacture in the Northern Roman Province. Cambridge University Press.

Williams, Wells. (1863).
The Chinese Commercial Guide. 5th edition p. 119. Hong Kong.

Woolley, Sir Leonard. (1930).
Digging up the Past. p. 66. Pelican.

Wulff, Hans E. (1966).
The Traditional Crafts of Persia. pp. 222, 224. The M.I.T. Press.

Yetts, W. Perceval. (1926).
"Discoveries of the Kozlov Expedition." *Burlington Magazine.* Vol. XLVIII, pp. 168. ff.